A
Mathematical
Dictionary

A Mathematical Dictionary

R.E. Jason Abdelnoor

Head of Mathematics Department,
Slatyford School, Newcastle upon Tyne

Wheaton

A Division of Pergamon Press

A. Wheaton & Company Limited
A Division of Pergamon Press
Hennock Road, Exeter EX2 8RP

Pergamon Press Ltd
Headington Hill Hall, Oxford OX3 0BW

Pergamon Press Inc.
Maxwell House, Fairview Park, Elmsford, New York 10523

Pergamon of Canada Ltd
Suite 104, 150 Consumers Road, Willowdale, Ontario M2J 1P9

Pergamon Press (Australia) Pty Ltd
P.O. Box 544, Potts Point, N.S.W. 2011

Pergamon Press GmbH
6242 Kronberg/Taunus, Pferdstrasse 1, Frankfurt-am-Main,
Federal Republic of Germany

First published 1979

Printed in Great Britain by A. Wheaton & Co. Ltd, Exeter

ISBN 0 08 021862 8 flexi
ISBN 0 08 021882 2 hard

Introduction

Mathematics is a language, and no one can think mathematically or express himself in mathematical terms unless he has first learnt the correct meaning of the words he has to use.

In recent years, with the development of modern mathematics, the scope of the subject has broadened considerably, and consequently the variety of words and concepts has increased. The function of this dictionary is to explain the mathematical terms now appearing in modern mathematics books and projects, covering the teaching ranges from the ages 11 to 16. It is a handy reference tool for the classroom, for the library and the home bookshelf.

How to use this book

The mathematical terms are set out alphabetically as in a normal dictionary. To understand one mathematical term it is often necessary to comprehend others with which it is linked. Cross-references to other terms that appear as separate entries are indicated by means of italic type. (In certain instances the italicised word may not match precisely the actual word defined, e.g. *graphical* would be intended to indicate the entry **Graph**.) In the example given below both the italicised words *angle* and *horizontal* are defined separately in the dictionary.

Sample

Depression

The angle of depression is the *angle* measured DOWNWARDS from the *horizontal* to an object.

Example:

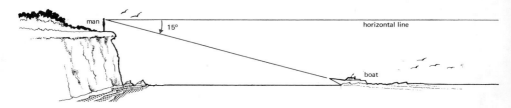

The angle of depression of the boat from the man is 15°.

To emphasise a particular feature in a diagram or an explanation, various words, lines or figures are printed in red, as shown in the example above.

Abacus

An abacus is apparatus used for counting.
Examples: These abaci are all used for counting in our *base* ten number system.

child's
abacus

Chinese
abacus showing
the numbers
00035614

Japanese abacus
showing the
numbers
00124589

This spike abacus
is used for
counting in
base five.

Acceleration

The acceleration of a body is the change in *speed* per unit of time.

Examples: A car is accelerating uniformly along a straight road and its speed is recorded every 5 seconds, as shown in this table:

speed, m/s	6	12	18	24	30
time, s	0	5	10	15	20

The constant acceleration over this period is

$$\frac{6\,\text{m/s}}{5\,\text{s}} = 1.2\ \text{m/s}^2$$

A sprinter in the Olympic Games reaches a speed of 36 km/h in the first 4 seconds of his race. His average acceleration over the first 4 seconds is

$$\frac{36\ \text{km/h}}{4\,\text{s}} = \frac{36\,000\ \text{m/h}}{4\,\text{s}}$$

$$= \frac{36\,000\ \text{m/s}}{60 \times 60 \times 4\,\text{s}}$$

$$= 2.5\ \text{m/s}^2$$

Acute

Acute means sharp. An acute *angle* is a sharply pointed angle whose size is between 0° and 90°.

Examples:

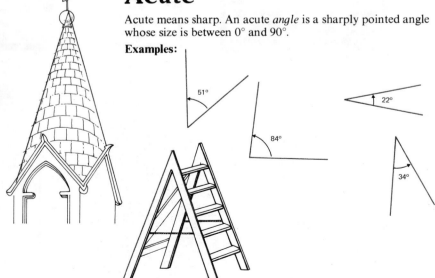

Additive inverse

The additive inverse is the *inverse* under addition. It is the number which, when added to the given number, gives the *identity element* for addition.

Examples:
The additive inverse of 3 is ⁻3, because 3 + ⁻3 = 0
The additive inverse of 5 is ⁻5, because 5 + ⁻5 = 0
The additive inverse of ⁻6 is 6, because ⁻6 + 6 = 0
The additive inverse of $-\frac{1}{2}$ is $\frac{1}{2}$, because $-\frac{1}{2} + \frac{1}{2} = 0$

NOTE: 0 is the identity for addition of numbers.
With *vectors* and *matrices* similar rules apply.

The additive inverse of $\begin{pmatrix} 3 \\ -5 \end{pmatrix}$ is $\begin{pmatrix} -3 \\ 5 \end{pmatrix}$, because

$$\begin{pmatrix} 3 \\ -5 \end{pmatrix} + \begin{pmatrix} -3 \\ 5 \end{pmatrix} = \begin{pmatrix} 0 \\ 0 \end{pmatrix}$$

The additive inverse of $\begin{pmatrix} 1 & 0 \\ -2 & 4 \end{pmatrix}$ is $\begin{pmatrix} -1 & 0 \\ 2 & -4 \end{pmatrix}$, because

$$\begin{pmatrix} 1 & 0 \\ -2 & 4 \end{pmatrix} + \begin{pmatrix} -1 & 0 \\ 2 & -4 \end{pmatrix} = \begin{pmatrix} 0 & 0 \\ 0 & 0 \end{pmatrix}$$

Affine transformations

Transformations which always *map parallel* lines onto parallel lines are called affine transformations.

Examples: *Shears* and *stretches* are affine transformations. Parallelism is *invariant* under these transformations.

The *similarities* are a *subset* of the affine transformations.

Examples: *Translations, reflections,* and *enlargements* are affine transformations.

All affine transformations of the *plane* can be represented by the *matrix* form

$$\begin{pmatrix} x' \\ y' \end{pmatrix} = \begin{pmatrix} a & b \\ c & d \end{pmatrix} \begin{pmatrix} x \\ y \end{pmatrix} + \begin{pmatrix} h \\ k \end{pmatrix}$$

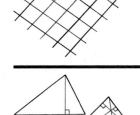

Altitude of a triangle

An altitude is the line from a *vertex* of a *triangle*, drawn *perpendicular* to the side opposite the vertex.

Examples (left): Some altitudes are shown in red.

An altitude may be inside or outside the triangle. There are three altitudes for each triangle, one from each vertex, and they all pass through the same point.

Angle

Angle between lines

An angle is the amount of turn from one line to another.

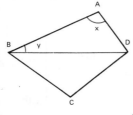

small angle

Examples: When any two straight lines meet at a point they form an angle. The point where the lines meet is called a *vertex*.

large angle

vertex

Angles are measured in degrees using a protractor.

Angles of a polygon

The angles of a *polygon* are the angles between the sides.

Examples: In the figure ABCD we can refer to angle x as Â or ∠A; but for angle y we must refer to it as AB̂D or ∠ABD not just B̂ or ∠B to avoid ambiguity.

The angles of the two polygons below are shown in red.

Direction of angles

Clockwise: this is the direction in which the hands on a clock turn.

Anticlockwise: this is the opposite direction.

10

Bearings are measured clockwise.

Rotations are called *positive* when they are anticlockwise.

Angle bisector   see **Bisector**

Anticlockwise   see **Angle**

Apex   see **Pyramid**

Arc

An arc is a line, straight or curved, which joins two points.

NOTE: In a *network* an arc joins two *nodes*.
There are six arcs in this network: p, q, r, s, t, and u.
There are three arcs between A and B.

NOTE: In a *circle*, a part of the *circumference* is called an arc.

The red part is an arc of the circle.

Area

The area is the size of a surface. The surface may be *plane* (flat) or curved.

Here are some ways of finding areas of important shapes:

Area of *Rectangle* = Length × Breadth.

Area of *Triangle* = $\frac{1}{2}$ Base × Height.

Area of *Parallelogram* = Base × Height.

Area of *Trapezium* = $\frac{1}{2}$ × (a + b) × Height.

Arithmetic mean

The arithmetic mean is what most people call the 'average'.
See **Mean**

Arrow diagrams

Arrow diagrams show a *relation* between *sets* of things, such as people or numbers. See **Correspondence**

Examples:

' — is the brother of —'

'—drinks—'

Arrowhead

An arrowhead is a *quadrilateral* that is NOT *convex* and has one *line of symmetry*.

Examples:

Associative

An *operation* is said to be associative, if it does not matter how *brackets* are put, when three *elements* are combined.

(a∗b)∗c = a∗(b∗c) is true if ∗ is associative.

Examples:

numbers under $\begin{cases} \text{addition and} \\ \text{multiplication} \end{cases}$ ARE associative

$$(2 + 3) + 5 = 2 + (3 + 5)$$
$$(4 \times 2) \times 3 = 4 \times (2 \times 3)$$

numbers under $\begin{cases} \textit{subtraction} \text{ and} \\ \textit{division} \end{cases}$ are NOT associative

$$(4 - 3) - 1 \neq 4 - (3 - 1)$$
$$(12 \div 6) \div 2 \neq 12 \div (6 \div 2)$$

matrices under $\begin{cases} \text{addition} \\ \text{multiplication} \end{cases}$ ARE associative.

Average

A teacher might ask for a typical member of the class to represent the group at chess, or football. An average is one member, or value, that represents the whole group. Mathematicians calculate three very important averages; they are *mean*, *median*, and *mode*.

Axis (plural Axes)

Axes are the reference lines on a *graph*. On a *coordinate* graph, the line going across has the x numbers and so is called the x-axis. The line going up the page has the y numbers and so is called the y-axis. The point where the lines cross is called the *origin* and represents *zero* on both axes.

NOTE: The *equation* of the x-axis is y = 0 because the y-coordinate is 0 for every point on it. Similarly the y-axis has equation x = 0.

Bar chart

Bar charts show information in a *graphical* form by the use of columns or bars. The length or height of the columns or bars corresponds to the size it represents. Rainfall graphs are often bar charts.

Example (left):

13

Base

When counting things we use groups.

Example (left): There are 2 groups of five sheep and 3 sheep on their own. So the number of sheep is here represented as 23_{five}. The base of a number is the size of the group used. The diagram shows counting in base five. The number of sheep is 23_{five}.

Examples: Our normal counting number system is called denary or base ten because the group size used is ten.
We use ten *digits*, 0, 1, 2, 3, 4, 5, 6, 7, 8, 9.
The place values are *multiples* of ten so that
the 6 in 7614 stands for 6×100
the 6 in 8563 stands for 6×10
352 stands for $(3 \times 100) + (5 \times 10) + (2 \times 1)$

We can count in other bases, such as base 6, using the digits 0, 1, 2, 3, 4, 5.
The group sizes are 6, $6 \times 6 \,(= 36)$, $6 \times 6 \times 6 \,(= 216)$
so that 3425 stands for
$(3 \times 216) + (4 \times 36) + (2 \times 6) + (5 \times 1) = 648 + 144 + 12 + 5$
$$(\text{in base ten})$$
$$= 809_{ten}$$

Bearing

The bearing of an object is the *angle* measured *clockwise* from north to the object.
Bearings always have three *digits*. 040° NOT JUST 40°.

Examples:

bearing of B
from A is
040°

bearing of C
from D is
230°

Binary numbers

Binary means two, so binary numbers are numbers in *base* two.
In the binary system only two *digits* are used: 0 and 1. The place values are

..	..	..	32	16	8	4	2	1	
						1	0	1_{two}	$= 5_{ten}$
					1	1	0	0_{two}	$= 12_{ten}$
				1	1	0	1	1_{two}	$= 27_{ten}$

Binary operation see Operation

Bisector

A bisector cuts something into two equal parts.

Examples:

a) A line which cuts an *angle* into two equal parts is called an angle bisector.

b) One line is a bisector of another line if it cuts it into two equal parts.

Line p is a bisector of line AB.

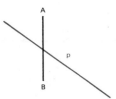

If the bisector of AB is also at *right-angles* to AB, the bisector is called the *perpendicular* bisector of AB. This line is sometimes called the *mediator* of AB.

NOTE: The mediator of AB is the *locus* of points P which are equidistant from A and B.

Boundary

The boundary of a figure is the line around the outside of the figure. The length of the boundary is called the *perimeter*.

Examples: The boundaries are shown in red.

football pitch

judo mat

mainland of England and Wales

15

Brackets

Brackets are used when three or more *elements* are combined by *operations*. Brackets tell you which two elements you combine first.

Example:
$$(10 - 7) + 2 = 3 + 2$$
$$= 5$$
but
$$10 - (7 + 2) = 10 - 9$$
$$= 1$$

Cancel

Cancelling a *fraction* is finding an *equivalent fraction* with smaller numbers. See **Equivalent Fractions**

Examples:

$$\frac{12}{15} = \frac{\cancel{3} \times 4}{\cancel{3} \times 5}$$ which cancels to $\frac{4}{5}$

$$\frac{14}{21} = \frac{\cancel{7} \times 2}{\cancel{7} \times 3}$$ which cancels to $\frac{2}{3}$

$$\frac{24}{32} = \frac{\cancel{8} \times 3}{\cancel{8} \times 4}$$ which cancels to $\frac{3}{4}$.

Centimetre

4 cm

A centimetre is one-hundredth of a *metre*.
1 cm $= \frac{1}{100}$ m and is this long ⊢————⊣
1 cm
NOTE: We shorten centimetre to cm

Examples:

This matchstick
is 4 cm long.

⊢————————————————————⊣

This line is 5 cm in length.

Centre of rotation

The centre of rotation is the one point which does not move when you do a *rotation*. Where tracing paper is used the centre of rotation is the point where you put your pen or compass point.

Examples:

The centres of rotation are shown in red.

Chord

A line joining two points of a *circle* is called a chord.

Examples:

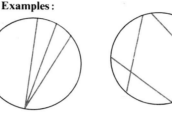

These lines show just SOME of the chords of this circle.

A chord passing through the centre of the circle is called a *diameter*.

There is only ONE diameter through A.

Circle

A circle is the *set* of all points in a *plane* at a fixed distance, the *radius*, from a fixed point, the centre.

radius

circumference

centre

Example (left): The *locus* of a conker being swung on the end of a piece of string is a circle.

For the *area* inside a circle, see **Pi**.
See also **Arc, Circumference, Sector, Segment, Semicircle**

Circumference

The circumference of a *circle* is the distance right around the circle. It is a special name for the *perimeter* of a circle.

Circumference $= \pi \times diameter$
$$C = \pi d \quad \text{(exactly)}$$

It is roughly 3 times the diameter.
$$C = 3 \times d \quad \text{(approximately)}$$

For π see **Pi**

Example (left): The circumference of this circle is approximately
$$3 \times 4 = 12 \text{ cm}$$

The circumference of a circle is also the distance rolled by a circle before coming the same way up again.

The circumference of this circle is shown by the length of the red line.

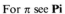

Clockwise see Angles

Closed

A *set* under the *operation* ∗ is closed when any two *elements* of the set combine to give another element of the set.

Examples:

$$\left\{ \begin{pmatrix} 1 & 0 \\ 0 & 1 \end{pmatrix}, \begin{pmatrix} ^-1 & 0 \\ 0 & 1 \end{pmatrix}, \begin{pmatrix} 1 & 0 \\ 0 & ^-1 \end{pmatrix}, \begin{pmatrix} ^-1 & 0 \\ 0 & ^-1 \end{pmatrix} \right\}$$

under multiplication is closed, because the *product* of any two *members* of the set is in the set.

$\{1, 2, 3, 4, 5, 6, 7, 8\}$ under addition is NOT closed because, for example, $4 + 5 = 9$ and 9 is NOT in the set.

However, $\{0, 1, 2, 3, 4\}$ under 'clock' addition is closed; as can be seen from this table:

$\oplus$	0	1	2	3	4
0	0	1	2	3	4
1	1	2	3	4	0
2	2	3	4	0	1
3	3	4	0	1	2
4	4	0	1	2	3

Coefficient

In a mathematical *expression* the coefficients are the numbers of each *variable*.

Example: In $5x + 3y$, 5 is called the coefficient of x, and 3 is called the coefficient of y.

Column

A list of numbers (or letters) going down the page is called a column.
Vectors are often written as a column.

Examples:

$$\begin{pmatrix} 2 \\ -3 \end{pmatrix} \qquad \begin{pmatrix} 1 \\ 4 \\ 0 \\ 5 \end{pmatrix} \qquad \begin{pmatrix} 2 \\ 0 \\ 1 \\ 7 \end{pmatrix}$$

When a *matrix* consists only of a column it is called a column matrix.

Commutative

An *operation* on a *set*, is commutative when it does not matter in which order the elements are combined. The operation * on a set is commutative if

$$a*b = b*a$$

for all *members* of the set.

Examples:

addition of numbers is commutative $\qquad 3 + 5 = 5 + 3$
and
multiplication of numbers is commutative $\qquad 7 \times 2 = 2 \times 7$
but,
division of numbers is NOT commutative $\qquad 3 \div 6 \neq 6 \div 3$
and
subtraction of numbers is NOT commutative $\qquad 4 - 2 \neq 2 - 4$

addition of *matrices* is commutative

$$\begin{pmatrix} 0 & 1 \\ 2 & 3 \end{pmatrix} + \begin{pmatrix} 4 & 7 \\ 0 & 1 \end{pmatrix} = \begin{pmatrix} 4 & 7 \\ 0 & 1 \end{pmatrix} + \begin{pmatrix} 0 & 1 \\ 2 & 3 \end{pmatrix}$$

but multiplication of matrices is *not* commutative

$$\begin{pmatrix} 1 & -1 \\ 2 & 1 \end{pmatrix}\begin{pmatrix} 3 & 0 \\ 1 & -1 \end{pmatrix} \neq \begin{pmatrix} 3 & 0 \\ 1 & -1 \end{pmatrix}\begin{pmatrix} 1 & -1 \\ 2 & 1 \end{pmatrix}$$

Complement of a set

The complement of a *set* A in *&* is the set of all *elements of &* NOT in A, and is shown by the *symbol* A'.

& **Example (left):**

If *&* = {1, 2, 3, 4, 5, 6, 7, 8, 9}
and A is the {*odd numbers*} = {1, 3, 5, 7, 9}
then A' is the {*even numbers*} = {2, 4, 6, 8}

The complement of A is the region shaded red.

NOTE: A *union* A' is the *universal set* A $\cup$ A' = *&*

Complementary angles

If two *angles* such as 63° and 27° add up to 90° they are called complementary angles and one is said to be the complement of the other.

27° + 63° = 90°

Cone

A cone is a solid which usually has a circular base and tapers to a point at the top, called its *vertex*.

Examples:

The *area* of the curved part of a cone is given by
curved area = π × *radius* × *slant height*
$$A = \pi r l$$

The *volume* of a cone is given by
volume = $\frac{1}{3}$ × base area × height
$$V = \frac{1}{3}\pi r^2 h$$

Congruent

If two objects have the same shape and size they are congruent.

Examples: Each cup and saucer (*left*) is congruent to every other cup and saucer.

◺ and ◹ are congruent shapes.

⌢ and ⌣ are congruent shapes.

▢ and ▢ are not the same size and so they are NOT congruent.

▭ and ▱ are not the same shape and so they are NOT congruent.

If congruent shapes have the same *sense*, then they are directly congruent; if they are congruent but there is a change in sense, then they are oppositely congruent.

Constant

A constant is a fixed number. Its value does not change.

Example: In the *formula* $s = 6t + 4$ the numbers 6 and 4 are constant, in contrast to s and t which can take different number values.

Continuous

How much do these apples weigh?

Weight is a continuous quantity, because the answer can be ANY value: 2.1841...kg
  or 2.1842...kg
  or 10.700701...kg

The spring balance measures a change in weight continuously but a scale pan using individual weights can only measure changes equal to the smallest weight.

Other continuous quantities are length, *area*, height, *volume*, temperature, and *speed*. As a car *accelerates* from start to 50 miles per hour, the speed must pass through ALL values between 0 and 50.

Quantities which are NOT continuous are called *discrete*.

NOTE: When x is continuous we use ALL the points on the number line.

$x > 3$

Convex

These *polygons* are called convex because all their *vertices* point outwards.

A shape is convex if the line joining ANY two points on the shape stays inside the shape.

Shapes which are NOT convex are called *re-entrant*.

Coordinates

A point on a *graph* can be fixed by a pair of numbers which describe its position with reference to the x and y *axes*.

Example: The point where the lines $x = 3$ and $y = 2$ cross is labelled (3, 2).
The coordinates of the point are 3 and 2.
The first number, 3, is called the x-coordinate.
The second number, 2, is called the y-coordinate.

NOTE: (2, 3) is NOT the same point as (3, 2). See **Ordered Pairs**

Correspondence

Arrow diagrams are classified into four types (called correspondences).

Examples:

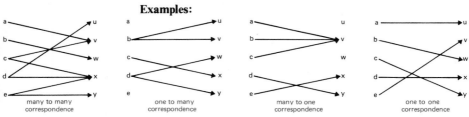

| many to many correspondence | one to many correspondence | many to one correspondence | one to one correspondence |

These *relations* are NOT *mappings*   These relations ARE mappings.

Corresponding points

Points are said to be corresponding when, under *transformations* such as *enlargement, rotation, reflection, translation* etc., one point is the *object* and the other is its *image*.

Examples:

A and A'
P and P' } are corresponding points.
Q and Q'

Cosine

The cosine of *angle* θ is written as $\cos \theta$

Cosine of angles less than 90°

$$\cos \theta = \frac{AB}{AC}$$

$$\cos \theta = \frac{\text{adjacent side}}{\text{hypotenuse}}$$

When the length of AC is 1 then
$$\cos \theta = AB$$

When this triangle is *enlarged*, with *scale factor* r,
$$PQ = r \cos \theta$$

Examples:

$\cos x = \frac{4}{5}$
$\cos x = 0.8$
$\cos 36.9° = 0.800$ (from tables)
$x = 36.9°$

$PQ = 3 \cos 60°$
$\quad = 3 \times 0.5$
$\quad = 1.5$

(cos 60° = 0.5 from tables)

Cosine of any angle

If a line OP of unit length turns through an angle θ from the x-*axis*; then the cosine of θ is the x-*coordinate* of P shown in red.

Cosine rule

When the lengths of the sides of a *triangle* are known, an angle, A, can be found by the rule

$$\cos A = \frac{b^2 + c^2 - a^2}{2bc}$$

When an angle and the two sides which form the angle are known, the third side can be found using the rule in this form

$$a^2 = b^2 + c^2 - 2bc \cos A$$

Counting numbers

The *set* of counting numbers is the set of numbers people first used to count things like sheep.

The set of counting numbers is $\{1, 2, 3, 4, 5, 6, 7, 8, \ldots\}$

The set of counting numbers is the same as the set of *natural numbers* and is a *subset* of the *integers*.

Cube

A cube is a *regular* solid with all its *faces square* and all its edges equal in length. The shape of a die is a cube.

2 cm   This is a diagram of a 2 cm cube.

Examples:

Cubed

A number 'cubed' is the number to the *power* 3.

Example: 2 cubed is $2^3 = 8$

Cubic centimetre

A cubic centimetre is a *unit* for measuring *volume*. Cubic centimetre is shortened to cm³

One cubic centimetre is the same volume as a *cube* whose edges are one *centimetre*.

Example: The volume of this cuboid is $2 \times 3 \times 7 = 42\,\text{cm}^3$

Cubic metre

A cubic metre is the standard unit for measuring *volume*. Cubic metre is shortened to m³

One cubic metre is the same volume as a *cube* whose edges are one *metre* in length.

Example: The volume of this *cuboid* is $\frac{1}{2} \times \frac{1}{2} \times 20 = 5\,\text{m}^3$

NOTE: $1\,\text{m}^3 = 100 \times 100 \times 100 \quad \text{cm}^3$

$1\,\text{m}^3 = 1\,000\,000 \quad \text{cm}^3$

Cuboid

A cuboid is a solid which has *rectangles* for all of its *faces*.

Examples:

Cumulative frequency

The cumulative frequency is the *sum* of the *frequencies* at or below a given value.

Example: In a survey 100 children were asked what size of shoe they wore.

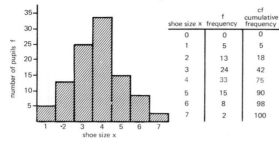

shoe size x	f frequency	cf cumulative frequency
0	0	0
1	5	5
2	13	18
3	24	42
4	33	75
5	15	90
6	8	98
7	2	100

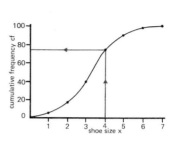

The frequency of shoe size 4 is 33 but there are 75 children with a shoe size of 4 or less. 75 is the cumulative frequency of size 4.

Cylinder

A cylinder is a *prism* with the shape of a *circle* along its length.

Examples:

The *area* of the curved part of the cylinder is given by

curved area = *circumference* × height

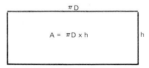

This can be opened into this

$$A = \pi D \times h$$

The *volume* of the cylinder is given by

volume = area of end × height

$$V = A \times h$$
$$V = \pi r^2$$

Data

Data are numbers which have been collected for study. Data can be displayed by *bar charts*, *pie charts*, *pictograms*, etc.

Example: A class of 23 pupils are asked how many children there

are in each of their families. The following data are collected
2, 1, 1, 2, 3, 3, 1, 2, 1, 4, 1, 2, 2, 3, 3, 3, 6, 4, 2, 3, 2, 2, 3.
There are five families with 1 child, eight families with 2 children,
seven families with 3 children, two families with 4 children and
just one family with 6 children.

Decagon

A decagon is a *polygon* with ten straight sides and ten *angles*.
Examples:

This is a *regular* decagon

Decimal fraction

A *fraction* with a *denominator* of 10, or 100, or 1000, or 10000. . .
is a decimal fraction.
Examples:

$$\frac{3}{10}, \quad \frac{17}{100}, \quad \frac{20}{100}, \quad \frac{427}{10000}$$

NOTE: They can be easily put into decimals

$$\frac{3}{10} = 0.3, \quad \frac{17}{100} = 0.17, \quad \frac{20}{100} = 0.20, \quad \frac{427}{10000} = 0.0427$$

Denominator see **Fraction**

Depression

The *angle* of depression is the angle measured DOWNWARDS from
the *horizontal* to an object.
Example:

The angle of depression of the boat from the man is 15°

Determinant

The determinant of a *matrix*, **M**, is a special number that goes with matrix, **M**. It can be found like this:

when $\mathbf{M} = \begin{pmatrix} a & b \\ c & d \end{pmatrix}$

then the determinant of **M** is ad − bc.

'the determinant of matrix **M**' is shortened to |**M**| or det **M**

Example:

$$\det \begin{pmatrix} 3 & 5 \\ 2 & 4 \end{pmatrix} = \begin{vmatrix} 3 & 5 \\ 2 & 4 \end{vmatrix}$$
$$= 3 \times 4 - 2 \times 5$$
$$= 2.$$

When the matrix is used to represent a *transformation* its determinant is the area *scale factor* of the transformation.

Diagonal

A diagonal is a straight line drawn from one *vertex* of a *polygon* (or solid figure) to another vertex.

Examples:

Diagonal of a polygon

All the diagonals are shown on this figure.

AC, AD, AE and AF are ALL the diagonals from A.

Diagonal of a polyhedron

The one and only diagonal from the vertex H is shown by the red line HK.

Diameter

A diameter of a *circle* is any line that joins two points of the circle and passes THROUGH THE CENTRE.

Examples:

All the diameters of a circle are the same length, twice the *radius*.

12 cm

6 cm

Difference

The difference of two numbers is the answer when the smaller number is *subtracted* from the bigger number.

Examples:

The difference between 8 and 3 is 5. $8 - 3 = 5$
and
The difference between 3 and 8 is 5. $8 - 3 = 5$.

Digit

A digit is any single figure used when representing a number. In our *base* ten number system that we use daily the digits are 0, 1, 2, 3, 4, 5, 6, 7, 8, 9.

Example: The digits used in 107 585 are 0, 1, 5, 7, 8.

Direct route

In a *network* of *nodes* and *arcs* a direct route between two nodes is a route that does not go through another node.

Example:

There are two direct routes, p and q, between the nodes A and B.
There is NO DIRECT route from D to B.

See Route Matrix

Directed numbers

Directed numbers show measuring or counting in two different directions.

Examples:

The *set* of numbers used for the higher readings are called *positive* and are sometimes marked with a $^+$ like this:
$\{^+1, \ ^+2, \ ^+3, \ ^+4, \ ^+5, \ ^+6, \ \ldots\}$

The set of numbers used for the lower readings are called *negative* and are marked with a $^-$ like this:
$\{^-1, \ ^-2, \ ^-3, \ ^-4, \ ^-5, \ ^-6, \ \ldots\}$

29

Discrete

When we ask the question 'How many?', we are looking at a discrete quantity. The answer must be exact and we usually use the *counting numbers*.

Examples: How many cars are there? The answer must be exact and in this case it must be a *whole number*.

How much money have I in my pocket? The answer must be exact, but in this case we count in hundredths of a pound. The answer may be £6.50, or £34.45, or £17.93, or £17.94, but NOT £17.931 863

NOTE: When x is discrete, we use only SOME of the points on the number line. For example x > 3 is shown by

Quantities which are NOT discrete are called *continuous*.

Displacement

A displacement (or *journey*) is a change in position. The displacement is defined by giving both the distance and the direction.

Example:

The displacement from the harbour A to the boat B is represented by the red line and can be defined
either as 5 km, *bearing* 037°
or as 3 km east, 4 km north.
Displacement is a *vector* quantity and so it can be best described using a vector.

Example: For the displacement Harbour to Boat shown above

$$\mathbf{AB} = \begin{pmatrix} 3 \\ 4 \end{pmatrix}$$

Distributive

When for a *set* of *elements*, {a, b, c, d,...} there are two binary *operations* such as * and ∘ then * is distributive over ∘ if
a * (b ∘ c) = (a * b) ∘ (a * c)

Examples:
a) With numbers × is distributive over +
   3 × (4 + 5) = (3 × 4) + (3 × 5)
b) With sets ∩ is distributive over ∪
   A ∩ (B ∪ C) = (A ∩ B) ∪ (A ∩ C)

Dividend

In a division the dividend is the number being divided.

Example:
In the division $\frac{5\,203}{4)20\,812}$ 20812 is the dividend

Divisor

In a division, the divisor is the number you are dividing by.

Example:
In the division $\frac{2014}{3)6042}$ the divisor is 3

Dodecagon

A *polygon* bounded by twelve straight lines and containing twelve *angles* is a dodecagon.

Examples:

This is a *regular* dodecagon.

Dodecahedron

A dodecahedron is a solid shape with twelve *faces*. All the faces of a *regular* dodecahedron are regular *pentagons*.

Example (left): This is a regular dodecahedron.

Domain

The domain of a *function* is the *set* of numbers *mapped* by the function.

NOTE: The domain is sometimes called the *object* set.

Example (left): {1, 2, 3, 4, 5} is the domain.

See **Range**

Duodecimal

$$t_{twelve} = 10_{ten}$$
$$14_{twelve} = 16_{ten}$$
$$18_{twelve} = 20_{ten}$$
$$21_{twelve} = 25_{ten}$$

A duodecimal number is a number written in *base* twelve. If we use the *symbols* t for ten and e for eleven then the *digits* in base twelve are 0, 1, 2, 3, 4, 5, 6, 7, 8, 9, t, e

Examples (left):

Element

The elements of a *set* are the things in the set.

Examples:
If A = {first 5 letters of the alphabet}, then the elements of A are a, b, c, d, and e.
If P = {prime numbers between 4 and 20}, then the elements of P are 5, 7, 11, 13, 17, and 19.
The number of elements in set A is five, this is written as
$$n(A) = 5$$
Similarly, $n(P) = 6$

Each letter or number in a *matrix* is also called an element.

Elevation

The *angle* of elevation is the angle measured UPWARDS from the *horizontal* to an object.

Example:

horizontal line

The angle of elevation of the kite from the man is 30°.

Empty set

When a *set* has no *elements* it is called the empty set and is shown as { }, or by the *symbol* ø

Example (left): If A = {6, 8, 10, 12} and B = {1, 3, 5, 7} then A ∩ B = { }, or A ∩ B = ø

The empty set is also called the *null set*.

Enlargement

Enlargement is a *transformation* which *maps* a shape onto a *similar* shape, from a centre O using a *scale factor* k.

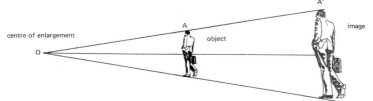

centre of enlargement

To find the *image*, A′, of a point A of the *object*, a line is drawn from O through A. A′ is then on OA and
OA′ = k × OA

In the example above the scale factor is 2.
The lines through O used to draw the image are called *pattern lines*.
When the scale factor k is a *fraction* then the image is smaller than the object.

When the scale factor k is *negative* then the enlarged image is also *rotated* 180° about O

Enlargement Matrix

The *transformation* $\begin{pmatrix} x \\ y \end{pmatrix} \rightarrow \begin{pmatrix} k & 0 \\ 0 & k \end{pmatrix} \begin{pmatrix} x \\ y \end{pmatrix}$ represents an enlargement with centre at the *origin*, and scale factor k.

NOTE: This scale factor, k, is the *linear scale factor*. The area scale factor is k^2, the *determinant* of the *matrix*.

a six

the total two

a total seven

Equally likely

Events are equally likely if the chance of them happening is the same.

Examples: If I roll a die, each of the six numbers is equally likely to show on top.
If I roll two dice and add the top numbers there are eleven possible totals, 2, 3, 4, 5, 6, 7, 8, 9, 10, 11, 12, and they are NOT equally likely. A 2 will only happen if I roll 1 and 1, but a total of 7 will come from many pairs—1 and 6, 2 and 5, 3 and 4, 4 and 3, 5 and 2, 6 and 1.

Equation

An equation is a statement using an equals sign.

Examples:

$y = 3x$ $\qquad$ $x + 4 = 7$

$y = x^2 - 5$ $\qquad$ $2x + 5 = 7x$

See **Expression**

Relation as an equation

An equation is one way of showing a *relation*.

Examples:

The *linear relation*	$x \rightarrow x + 3$
can be written as the *linear equation*	$y = x + 3$
The *quadratic relation*	$x \rightarrow x^2 + 2$
can be written as the equation	$y = x^2 + 2,$

(this is NOT called a 'quadratic' equation).

See **Equation of a Line, Linear Equation, Quadratic Equation, Simultaneous Equations, Solution of an Equation**

Equation of a line

The equation of a line is the *relation* satisfied by the *coordinates* of the points of the line.

As the first coordinate, x, is 3 for every point on the line the *equation* of this line is x = 3.

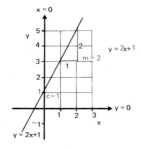

As the two coordinates always add up to 7 for the points on this line, its equation is
$$x + y = 7$$

NOTE: The equation of the x-*axis* is $y = 0$ and the equation of the y-axis is $x = 0$.

Any straight line on a *graph* represents a *linear equation* which can be written in the form $y = mx + c$

Examples:

$y = 3x - 4$ $y = x + 1$

$y = 8 - x$ $y = 2 - \frac{1}{2}x$

When a linear equation is written in the form $y = mx + c$ the number m represents the *gradient* of the line and the number c represents the intercept on the y-*axis*.

Equilateral triangle

An equilateral triangle is a *triangle* with all three sides the same length.

Examples:

NOTE: If all three sides of a triangle are equal, the *angles* will be equal and will be 60°.

Equivalent fractions

Fractions are equivalent if they can be *cancelled* to the same fraction.

Example: $\frac{8}{12}$ and $\frac{6}{9}$ are equivalent because they can both be cancelled to $\frac{2}{3}$.

Here are two *sets* of equivalent fractions:

$$\left\{\frac{1}{2}, \ \frac{2}{4}, \ \frac{4}{8}, \ \frac{5}{10}, \ \frac{8}{16}, \ \frac{10}{20}\right\}$$
$$\left\{\frac{5}{6}, \ \frac{50}{60}, \ \frac{10}{12}, \ \frac{25}{30}, \ \frac{500}{600}\right\}$$

If $\frac{a}{b}$ is any fraction then $\frac{ka}{kb}$ is an equivalent fraction where k is a number not equal to *zero*.

Euler's formula

Euler's *formula* applies to *networks* and to *polyhedra*.

For networks:

$$nodes + regions = arcs + 2$$
$$N + R = A + 2$$

Example:

There are 4 nodes A B C and D
There are 7 arcs p, q, r, s, t, u, v
There are 5 regions shown i, ii, iii, iv, vi
$$4 + 5 = 7 + 2$$

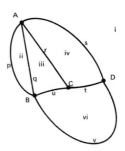

For polyhedra:

$$vertices + faces = edges + 2$$
$$V + F = E + 2$$

Example: A *cube* has 8 vertices, 6 faces, 12 edges.
$$8 + 6 = 12 + 2$$

Evaluate

Evaluate means 'find the value of'.

Example: 'Evaluate 2a + b when a = 7, and b = 6'.

$$
\begin{aligned}
2a + b &= 2 \times a + b \\
&= 2 \times 7 + 6 \\
&= 14 + 6 \\
&= 20
\end{aligned}
$$

Even numbers

Even numbers are numbers that can be divided exactly by 2. Even numbers are numbers ending in 0 or 2 or 4 or 6 or 8.

Examples: These are even numbers:

24, 750, 38, 6, 7914, 2908, 3100, 14.

The even numbers are the *multiples* of 2.

Expression

A collection of numbers and *symbols* and letters with NO equals sign, is called an expression.

Examples:

2x + 5 + 7x
a + b + 3b − a
2 sin x
$x^2 + 1$

Statements which DO have an equals sign are called *equations*.

Face

The flat sides of a *polyhedron* are called faces.

Examples:

This *pyramid* has five faces, four sides and one base.

This solid has six faces.

This *prism* has five faces.

Factorise

When we use the *distributive* law backwards we call it factorising.

Examples:
ab + ac = a(b + c)
3x + 3y = 3(x + y)
7 × 53 + 7 × 47 = 7 × (53 + 47) = 7 × 100
PR + QR = (P + Q)R
$(A \cap B) \cup (A \cap C) = A \cap (B \cup C)$

Factors

The factors of a number are those numbers which divide exactly into the number.

Example: The factors of 24 are 1, 2, 3, 4, 6, 8, 12, 24.

See **Prime Factors**

NOTE:

Pair of factors

The pairs of factors of 30 are $1 \times 30, 2 \times 15, 3 \times 10, 5 \times 6$

Set of factors

The *set* of factors of 30 are $\{1, 2, 3, 5, 6, 10, 15, 30\}$

Prime factors

The *prime* factors of 30 are $\{2, 3, 5\}$

Fibonacci numbers

A Fibonacci number is one from this *set* of numbers
$$\{ 1, \quad 1, \quad 2, \quad 3, \quad 5, \quad 8, \quad 13, \quad 21, \quad \ldots \}$$
$$1 + 1 = 2$$
$$1 + 2 = 3$$
$$2 + 3 = 5$$
$$3 + 5 = 8$$

Each number is the *sum* of the two numbers before it.

Formula

A formula is a general *equation*. It shows the connection between related quantities.

Example: The *perimeter* P of a *rectangle* with sides a and b is given by the formula
$$P = 2a + 2b$$

Some examples of formulas you may meet are:

$$v = u + at, \quad C = \pi d, \quad T = 2\pi \sqrt{\frac{l}{g}}, \quad \frac{1}{f} = \frac{1}{v} + \frac{1}{u},$$

$$A = \pi r^2, \text{ and } Euler's\ formula.$$

Fraction

A fraction is a number less than 1, such as

$$\frac{1}{2} \qquad \frac{1}{4} \qquad \frac{3}{5} \qquad \frac{11}{13} \qquad \frac{21}{40}$$

Example (left): $\dfrac{\text{number of shaded parts}}{\text{number of parts of circle}} = \frac{3}{8}$

The shaded portion of the *circle* is $\frac{3}{8}$ of the whole circle.

NOTE: The bottom number is called the *denominator* and the top number is called the *numerator*.

See **Decimal Fraction, Equivalent Fractions, Fraction Point, Improper Fraction, Percentage Fraction**

Fraction point

A dot is used to separate *whole numbers* and *fractions* when writing a number using place notation. The dot is called a fraction point.

Examples: $17\frac{9}{10}$ could be written 17.9_{ten}

$2\frac{3}{5}$ could be written 2.3_{five}

$3\frac{1}{4}$ could be written 11.01_{two}

Frequency

The frequency of an event is how many times it has happened.

Example: A die is rolled 100 times and a six comes up 13 times. The frequency of a score six is 13.

See **Mode**

Frequency diagram

A frequency diagram is a *bar chart* showing *frequency*. In it the height of the bars shows the frequency of each event.

Example: A die is rolled 130 times.

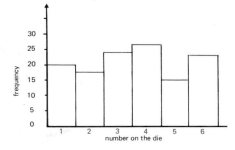

Function

$$x \xrightarrow{f} x^2$$
$$^+2 \searrow$$
$$^-2 \nearrow 4$$
$$3 \rightarrow 9$$
$$4 \rightarrow 16$$

Functions are special kinds of *relations* in which each *object* is *mapped onto* only ONE *image*.
They are also known as *mappings*.

Examples:
f (*left*) is a function as every object has only ONE image

$$x \xrightarrow{g} \text{square root of } x$$
$$1 \rightarrow {}^+1 \text{ or } {}^-1$$
$$4 \rightarrow {}^+2 \text{ or } {}^-2$$
$$9 \rightarrow {}^+3 \text{ or } {}^-3$$

However, g (*above*) is NOT a function as there is more than one image for each object.
See **Correspondence** and **Mapping**

Glide reflection

The glide reflection is the single *transformation* that will replace the combined transformations: a *translation parallel* to line m and a *reflection* in line m, taken in either order.

Examples:

G(A) is the *image* after the glide reflection: reflect in $y = 0$ and translate $\binom{5}{0}$

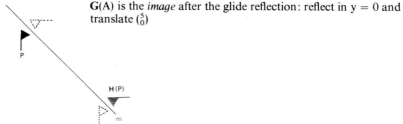

H(P) is the image after the glide reflection: translate parallel to m and reflect in line m.

Gradient

The gradient of a line is a measurement of how 'steep' it is. The gradient of a line can be found by drawing *right-angled triangles* on the line.

$$\text{Gradient of line AB} = \frac{\text{rise}}{\text{tread}}$$

$$= \tan \theta$$

Example:
Gradient of $y = 2x$ is
$$\frac{\text{rise}}{\text{tread}} = \frac{6}{3} = \frac{2}{1} = 2$$

Gram

A gram is a *unit* of mass. A gram weight is the weight of a mass of one gram. (A large pea is about one gram weight.) The abbreviation for gram is g

Example:

A spoon has a mass of
17 grams, that is, 17 g

Graph

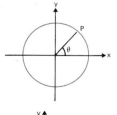

A graph is a way of illustrating information and numbers on paper to make it more easily understood.
Data is often displayed by *bar charts*, *pie charts*, *frequency diagrams*, *histograms*, and *pictograms*.
In other situations *axes* and *coordinates* are used.

Hemisphere

A hemisphere is half a *sphere*, formed by a *plane of symmetry* of the sphere.

Examples:

Heptagon

A heptagon is a *polygon* bounded by 7 straight lines and containing 7 *angles*.

Examples:

This is a *regular* heptagon.

Hexagon

A hexagon is a *polygon* bounded by 6 straight lines and containing 6 *angles*.

Examples:

This is a *regular* hexagon.

Highest common factor

Two *counting numbers* always have 1 as a common *factor*. Often they will have other factors in common.

Example:
{factors of 12} = {1, 2, 3, 4, 6, 12}
{factors of 15} = {1, 3, 5, 15}
1 and 3 are the only common factors of 12 and 15.

The highest common factor (usually abbreviated to HCF) is the largest of these numbers, in this case 3.

Example:
{factors of 20} = {1, 2, 4, 5, 10, 20}
{factors of 30} = {1, 2, 3, 5, 6, 10, 15, 30}
10 is the highest common factor of 20 and 30.

Histogram

A histogram is similar to a *frequency diagram*, but it is the *area* of the bars and not the height that shows the *frequency*.

Example: The table shows the frequency f of families with x children in the family.

x	f
0	7
1	10
2	16
3	12
4	8
5	3
6 to 10	10

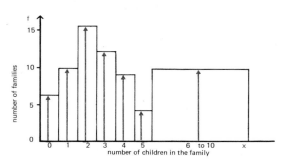

This is a frequency diagram

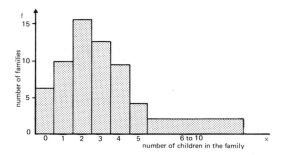

This is a histogram for the same information.

Horizontal

A line is horizontal if it is *parallel* to the Earth's skyline.

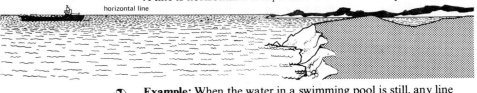

horizontal line

Example: When the water in a swimming pool is still, any line on its surface is horizontal.

Hypotenuse

The hypotenuse is the side opposite the *right-angle* in a *right-angled triangle*. It is also the longest side in a right-angled triangle.

Examples:

hypotenuse

hypotenuse

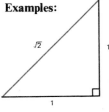

$\sqrt{2}$

1

1

The hypotenuse is $\sqrt{2}$

3 cm

5 cm

4 cm

The hypotenuse is 5 cm

Icosahedron

An icosahedron is a solid with twenty *faces*.
In a *regular* icosahedron each face is an *equilateral triangle*.

Example (right):
This is a regular icosahedron.

Identical

Shapes and objects are identical if they are exactly the same shape and size.

In some *transformations*, such as *reflection* and *rotation*, the *object* and *image* are identical. These transformations are called the *isometries*.

MUG making machine

Tessellations show patterns with one or more identical shapes, which fit together, without gaps, to fill space.

See **Congruent**

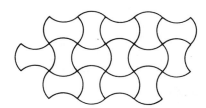

Identity element

An identity is an *element* which when combined with other elements, leaves them the same. The identity depends on the *set* of elements and the *operation*.

Examples:

For numbers

and the operation ×
  it is 1
  $3 \times 1 = 3$
  $2 \times 1 = 2$
  $1 \times 5 = 5$
  $^-6 \times 1 = {}^-6$
  $1 \times 4 = 4$

and the operation +
  it is 0
  $0 + 3 = 3$
  $2 + 0 = 2$
  $0 + 5 = 5$
  $^-6 + 0 = {}^-6$
  $9 + 0 = 9$

For sets

and the operation ∪
  it is ø
  $A \cup ø = A$
  $ø \cup B = B$

and the operation ∩
  it is $\mathscr{E}$
  $P \cap \mathscr{E} = P$
  $\mathscr{E} \cap Q = Q$

For 2 by 2 matrices

and the operation $\begin{pmatrix} 0 & 0 \\ 0 & 0 \end{pmatrix}$
addition, it is

and the operation $\begin{pmatrix} 1 & 0 \\ 0 & 1 \end{pmatrix}$
multiplication, it is

Identity mapping

The identity mapping is the *mapping* that *maps* each *element* onto itself.

Identity transformation

The identity transformation is the *transformation* that *maps* each point of the *plane* onto itself. Under the identity transformation a shape remains unchanged and all properties of the shape are *invariant*.

When *matrices* are used to represent transformations in the plane, the identity transformation is represented by the matrix $\begin{pmatrix} 1 & 0 \\ 0 & 1 \end{pmatrix}$

Image

The image is the result when an *object* is *transformed*.

Examples: The shape S′ is the image in each case.

object   image

Here the image is the result of a *reflection*.

Here the image is the result of a *rotation* about 0.

The image is also the result when a number undergoes a *mapping*.

Examples:

$x \rightarrow x + 2$
$3 \rightarrow 5$
$2 \rightarrow 4$ the image of 3 is 5
$5 \rightarrow 7$ the image of 1 is 3
$1 \rightarrow 3$ the image of 6 is 8
$0 \rightarrow 2$
$6 \rightarrow 8$

NOTE: The *set* of images {5, 4, 7, 3, 2, 8} is called the image set.

See **Corresponding Points**

Improper fraction

An improper fraction is a *fraction* with the *numerator* bigger than the *denominator* such as

$$\frac{5}{3}, \quad \frac{7}{4}, \quad \frac{10}{9}, \quad \frac{16}{13}, \quad \frac{8}{5}, \quad \frac{11}{5}$$

These improper fractions can be rewritten as *mixed numbers.*

Examples:

$$\frac{4}{3} = 1\frac{1}{3}, \qquad \frac{8}{5} = 1\frac{3}{5}$$
$$\frac{11}{4} = 2\frac{3}{4}, \qquad \frac{15}{2} = 7\frac{1}{2}$$

Incidence matrix

An incidence *matrix* relates *nodes, arcs, regions,* and other properties of a *network.*

Example:

The nodes are lettered A, B, C, and D
The arcs are numbered 1, 2, 3, 4, and 5

For this network the incidence of nodes on arcs is shown by the matrix

$$
\mathbf{P} = \begin{array}{c} \\ A \\ B \\ C \\ D \end{array}
\begin{pmatrix}
1 & 2 & 3 & 4 & 5 \\
2 & 1 & 0 & 0 & 0 \\
0 & 1 & 1 & 1 & 0 \\
0 & 0 & 1 & 1 & 1 \\
0 & 0 & 0 & 0 & 1
\end{pmatrix}
$$

The *transpose* of **P**, **P′**, shows the incidence of arcs on nodes. The matrix *product* **PP′** is the same as the *route matrix* **R** for the nodes A, B, C, and D, except that the *leading diagonal* is different.

$$
\mathbf{PP'} =
\begin{pmatrix}
2 & 1 & 0 & 0 & 0 \\
0 & 1 & 1 & 1 & 0 \\
0 & 0 & 1 & 1 & 1 \\
0 & 0 & 0 & 0 & 1
\end{pmatrix}
\begin{pmatrix}
2 & 0 & 0 & 0 \\
1 & 1 & 0 & 0 \\
0 & 1 & 1 & 0 \\
0 & 1 & 1 & 0 \\
0 & 0 & 1 & 1
\end{pmatrix}
=
\begin{pmatrix}
3 & 1 & 0 & 0 \\
1 & 3 & 2 & 0 \\
0 & 2 & 3 & 1 \\
0 & 0 & 1 & 1
\end{pmatrix}
$$

$$
\text{but} \quad \mathbf{R} =
\begin{pmatrix}
2 & 1 & 0 & 0 \\
1 & 0 & 2 & 0 \\
0 & 2 & 0 & 1 \\
0 & 0 & 1 & 0
\end{pmatrix}
$$

Index form

A number x written as the *power* of another number, a, is said to be in index form.

$49 = 7^2$
$16 = 2^4$
$10000 = 10^4$
$125 = 5^3$
$0.01 = 10^{-2}$

If $x = a^n$ then n is the index, showing the power of a.

Examples (left):

These numbers are written in index form; the indices are shown in red.

Inequality

An inequality is a statement showing one quantity is NOT equal to another quantity.

$a < b$ means 'a is less than b'
$a > b$ means 'a is greater than b'
$a \neq b$ means 'a is unequal to b'

Examples:

From the dots on the number line (*left*) it can be seen that

$4 > 1$	$1 < 4$
$1 > {}^-2$	${}^-2 < 1$
${}^-2 > {}^-5$	${}^-5 < {}^-2$

The *solution* to the inequality $x < 3$ is shown by the red line.

See **Directed Numbers, Solution Set**

Integers

The *set* of integers is $\{ \ldots {}^-4, {}^-3, {}^-2, {}^-1, 0, 1, 2, 3, \ldots \}$

The set of integers is a *subset* of the set of the *rationals*.

The set of *counting numbers* is a subset of the set of integers.

Interquartile range

The interquartile range is the *range* of the *data* between the first and the third *quartiles*. It is usually found from a *cumulative frequency* diagram.

Example (left):

The interquartile range is $63 - 31 = 32$ marks

The semi-interquartile range is $\frac{1}{2} \times (63 - 31) = 16$ marks.

48

Intersect

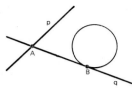

Lines and curves intersect if they cross or touch.

Examples:
Lines p and q (*left*) intersect at A;
the *circle* and line q intersect at B;
but the line p and the circle do not intersect.

Lines $y = 2x$
and $x + y = 3$
intersect at the point (1, 2).

Point (2, 3) is the intersection of line $x = 2$ and line $y = 3$.

Intersection

The intersection of two *sets* A and B is the set that has in it, only those *elements*, and all those elements, that are in both set A and set B.

Example:
If $A = \{2, 4, 6, 8\}$
and $B = \{1, 2, 4, 8\}$
then $A \cap B = \{2, 4, 8\}$

The intersection of sets is shown by the symbol $\cap$

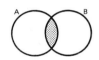

On a *Venn diagram*, the intersection of set A and set B is shown by the set of points shaded red. $A \cap B$ is shaded red.

Invariants

Invariants are facts that remain the same after a *transformation*. Invariants are often properties of the *object* and *image* that are the same both BEFORE and AFTER the transformation, such as length, *area*, *angles*, *parallel* lines, straightness, number of *arcs*, and *sense*.

Examples:
For a *topological transformation*, some invariants are *order of nodes*, number of arcs and *regions*, and number of nodes.

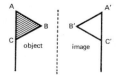

For a *reflection*, some invariants are straightness, size of angle, area, and number of regions. But sense is changed so this is not an invariant.

Inverse element

The inverse of an *element* is the element which combines with it to give the *identity*.

If a *set* has no *identity element* under an *operation*, then there are NO inverses.

Examples:

For numbers under addition:

the inverse of 6 is $^-6$ because $6 + {}^-6 = 0$ ⎰and because 0 is

the inverse of 3 is $^-3$ because $3 + {}^-3 = 0$ ⎱the identity for

the inverse of $^-1$ is 1 because $^-1 + 1 = 0$ ⎱numbers under addition.

For 2 by 2 *matrices* and multiplication:

the inverse of $\begin{pmatrix} 3 & 1 \\ 5 & 2 \end{pmatrix}$ is $\begin{pmatrix} 2 & ^-1 \\ ^-5 & 3 \end{pmatrix}$

because $\begin{pmatrix} 3 & 1 \\ 5 & 2 \end{pmatrix}\begin{pmatrix} 2 & ^-1 \\ ^-5 & 3 \end{pmatrix} = \begin{pmatrix} 1 & 0 \\ 0 & 1 \end{pmatrix}$

the inverse of $\begin{pmatrix} 1 & 0 \\ 7 & 6 \end{pmatrix}$ is $\frac{1}{6}\begin{pmatrix} 6 & 0 \\ ^-7 & 1 \end{pmatrix}$

because $\begin{pmatrix} 1 & 0 \\ 7 & 6 \end{pmatrix}\begin{pmatrix} 1 & 0 \\ -\frac{7}{6} & \frac{1}{6} \end{pmatrix} = \begin{pmatrix} 1 & 0 \\ 0 & 1 \end{pmatrix}$

and because $\begin{pmatrix} 1 & 0 \\ 0 & 1 \end{pmatrix}$ is the identity for 2 by 2 matrices and multiplication.

If $\mathbf{M} = \begin{pmatrix} a & b \\ c & d \end{pmatrix}$ then,

the inverse of $\mathbf{M}$ is $\mathbf{M}^{-1} = \dfrac{1}{\det \mathbf{M}}\begin{pmatrix} d & ^-b \\ ^-c & a \end{pmatrix}$ where

$\det \mathbf{M}$ is the *determinant* of the matrix $\mathbf{M}$.

Inverse function

As the words *function* and *mapping* have the same meaning, an inverse function is the same as an *inverse mapping*.

See **Inverse Mapping**

Inverse mapping

For a *mapping* f that *maps* each point x onto its *image*, y, the inverse mapping f^{-1} is the mapping that maps each point y of the *image set* back onto x.

Example: For $x \xrightarrow{\ f\ } 2x$ the inverse mapping is $x \xrightarrow{\ f^{-1}\ } \frac{1}{2}x$

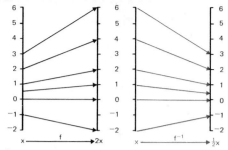

NOTE: A *function* f is either a MANY to ONE or a ONE to ONE *correspondence*; BUT f can only have an *inverse function* if f is a ONE to ONE correspondence.

Inverse pair

If an *element* has an *inverse* under an *operation*, then the element and its inverse are an inverse pair.

Examples: Some inverse pairs for numbers under addition are
$(6, {}^-6)$, $({}^-2, 2)$, $(\frac{1}{3}, {}^-\frac{1}{3})$, $({}^-1, 1)$

When an element is its own inverse, the element is called self inverse.

Example:

$$\begin{pmatrix} {}^-1 & 0 \\ 0 & {}^-1 \end{pmatrix} \begin{pmatrix} {}^-1 & 0 \\ 0 & {}^-1 \end{pmatrix} = \begin{pmatrix} 1 & 0 \\ 0 & 1 \end{pmatrix} \text{ so } \begin{pmatrix} {}^-1 & 0 \\ 0 & {}^-1 \end{pmatrix} \text{ is self inverse.}$$

Inverse transformation

For a *transformation* **M** which *maps* point P onto its *image* P′, the inverse transformation $\mathbf{M}^{-1}$ is the transformation which maps P′ back onto P, for all points.

Example: The transformation **E**: *enlargement* with *scale factor* 2 about O, has the inverse transformation $\mathbf{E}^{-1}$: enlargement with scale factor $\frac{1}{2}$ about O.

NOTE: If a transformation is represented by the *matrix* **A**, then the inverse transformation when it exists is represented by the *inverse* matrix $\mathbf{A}^{-1}$.

Irrational numbers

An irrational number is a number that cannot be written as a fraction, $\frac{p}{q}$, where p and q are *integers* and q is not *zero*.

See **Rational**

Examples:

$\sqrt{2} = 1.414\ldots$
$\pi = 3.14159265\ldots$
$\sqrt{10} = 3.1623\ldots$
$(\sqrt{7} + 8) = 10.6458\ldots$

When irrational numbers are expressed as decimals, they do NOT *terminate* or *recur*.

The *symbol* I is sometimes used for the *set* of irrational numbers. The *union* of the *rational* numbers and the irrational numbers is the set of *real numbers*.

$I \cup Q = R$

Isometric

Isometric paper is paper covered with a *tessellation* of *equilateral triangles*.

Example: This is $\frac{1}{2}$ cm isometric paper. Each side of every triangle is $\frac{1}{2}$ cm

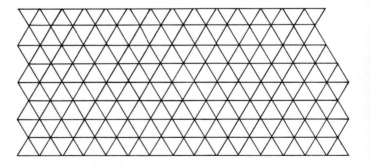

Isometries

Isometries are the *transformations* in which all lengths are *invariant*.

Examples: *Rotations*, *reflections*, and *translations* are isometries.
An isometry in which *sense* is invariant is called a direct isometry, and an isometry which doesn't preserve sense is called an opposite isometry.
After the *identity transformation*, the isometries are the simplest transformations for they *map* figures of the same shape and size.

See **Similarities**

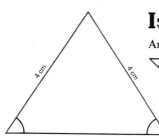

Isosceles

An isosceles *triangle* is one with two sides of equal length.

There are two equal *angles* in an isosceles triangle.

Journey

A journey is another word for a *displacement*.

Kilogram

A kilogram is the standard *unit* of mass. It is equal to 1000 *grams*. We shorten kilogram to kg

Examples:
A bag of potatoes may be 2 kg in weight

A man may be 70 kg in weight

1000 g = 1 kg
1000 kg = 1 *tonne*

Kilometre

A kilometre is a length of 1000 *metres*. We shorten kilometre to km. One kilometre is a distance of a little over $\frac{1}{2}$ a mile.

Example: The red line shows 1 kilometre.

Kite

A kite is a *quadrilateral* with two pairs of equal sides which are not opposite to each other.

Examples:

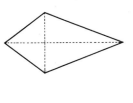

The *diagonals* of a kite cross at *right-angles*.
A kite only has one *line of symmetry*. AB is a line of symmetry but PQ is not.

Latitude

A parallel of latitude is a *circle* on the surface of the earth, with a centre on the line joining north and south poles. These circles are all *parallel* to each other and so are called parallels of latitude.

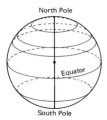

To describe any point P on the parallel of latitude shown in red we use the *angle* between the two *radii* of the earth OP and OE. O is the centre of the earth and E is the point on the equator so that P and E are on the same line of *longitude*. The red circle is called the parallel of latitude 50°N. Other parallels are similarly labelled.

LCM   see **Lowest Common Multiple**

Leading diagonal

In a table or *matrix* which is *square*, the line of numbers or letters going from the top left corner to the bottom right corner, is called the leading diagonal.

Examples:

Line segment

A line segment is a part of a straight line between two given points.

Example:

AB is a line segment

Line symmetry

A line of *symmetry* on a shape is a line which can be used as a fold, so that one half of the shape covers the other half exactly. A shape may have one or more lines of symmetry.

Examples:

one line of
symmetry

two lines of
symmetry

three lines of
symmetry

no line of
symmetry

Line symmetry is also called reflective symmetry because a mirror *reflection* on the line will produce the whole shape.

Linear equation

A linear equation with ONE unknown (letter) is an *equation* which can be written in the form
$ax + b = 0$

Examples:
$3x + 4 = 7$ $2x + 6 = x - 2$
These equations can have only ONE *solution*.

When a linear equation is used to show a *linear relation*, the equation can be written with the two unknowns x and y in the form
$y = ax + b$
In this case there are many solutions. See **Equation of a Line**

Linear relations

Linear relations are *relations* which can be written in the form
$x \rightarrow ax + b$. When *ordered pairs* for a linear relation are plotted on a *graph* they form a straight line.

Examples: Here are some linear relations

$x \rightarrow x + 2$

$x \rightarrow 3x$

$x \rightarrow 4x - 1$

$x \rightarrow 5 - \frac{1}{2}x$

Linear scale factor see Scale Factor

Litre

A litre is a *unit* of *volume* equal to 1000 *cubic centimetres*. We sometimes shorten litre to l, so long as there is no confusion with the number 1.

Examples:
1 pint is just over 0.5 litres

4 gallons is nearly 20 litres

Locus (plural Loci)

The locus is the line or 'path' of a *set* of points that follow some rule or law.

Example:
If Q is a fixed point and {P: PQ is 2 cm} then the locus of P is a *circle*.

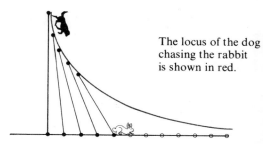

The locus of the dog
chasing the rabbit
is shown in red.

The locus of the man as the ladder slips down is shown in red.

Logarithm function

The logarithm function is the *inverse* of a growth *function*.

If $x \xrightarrow{f} a^x$ then $x \xrightarrow{f^{-1}} \log_a x$
(We shorten logarithm to log)

Example: For the growth function $x \rightarrow 2^x$ the inverse function
is $x \rightarrow \log_2 x$

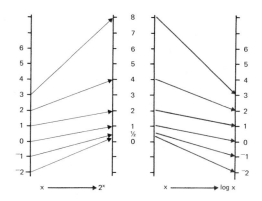

In the above example the logarithm function is to *base* 2; because
we count in a base ten number system, for computation work
we only use the logarithm function to base 10.

$x \rightarrow \log_{10} x$

which is the inverse function of $x \rightarrow 10^x$.

Examples:

$x \rightarrow 10^x$	$x \rightarrow \log x$
$2 \rightarrow 10^2$	$100 \rightarrow 2$
$3 \rightarrow 10^3$	$1000 \rightarrow 3$
$^-1 \rightarrow 0.1$	$0.1 \rightarrow {}^-1$
$0.301 \rightarrow 10^{0.301}$	
$0.301 \rightarrow 2$	$2 \rightarrow 0.301$

Longitude

A line of longitude is half a *circle* on the surface of the Earth with one end at the South Pole and one end at the North Pole.

To describe any point **P** on the line of longitude shown in red we use the *angle* between the *radii* **OG** and **OH**. O is the centre of the Earth, G and H are points on the equator, and H is also on the red line of longitude. G is always on the black line of longitude called the Greenwich meridian. It is a fixed line of longitude passing through Greenwich, London. The red line is the line of longitude 80°E. Other lines of longitude are similarly labelled.

Lowest common multiple

For two (or more) numbers a and b, the common *multiples* are those numbers which appear in both the *set* of multiples of a and the set of multiples of b.

Example:
{multiples of 2} = {2, 4, 6, 8, 10, 12, 14, 16, 18, 20, 22, 24,...}
{multiples of 3} = {3, 6, 9, 12, 15, 18, 21, 24, 27,...}
{common multiples of 2 and 3} = {6, 12, 18, 24,...}

The lowest common multiple (usually abbreviated to LCM) is the smallest of the common multiples.

Examples:
The LCM of 2 and 3 is 6
The LCM of 4 and 8 is 8
The LCM of 10 and 15 is 30
The LCM of 5 and 7 is 35

Mapping

A mapping is a *relation* in which for each *object mapped* there is only ONE *image*.

Examples (left and right):

See **Correspondence** and **Function**

Mapping diagram

A mapping diagram is a diagram to show a *mapping*. We can use a *relation diagram* to do this but usually we use two number lines and arrows.

Example (left):

Maps (onto)

A *transformation* maps an *object* onto its *image*.

Example: point A, (1, 2) is MAPPED ONTO point A', (3, 6) by the translation $\binom{2}{4}$

Matrix (plural **Matrices**)

A matrix is an array of numbers or letters in the shape of a *rectangle*.

Examples:

$$\begin{pmatrix} 1 & 0 & 0 & 1 \\ 0 & 2 & 1 & 1 \\ 0 & 1 & 0 & 3 \\ 1 & 1 & 3 & 0 \end{pmatrix} \quad \begin{pmatrix} 1 & 2 \\ 7 & \frac{2}{3} \end{pmatrix} \quad \begin{pmatrix} a & d \\ b & a \\ a & c \end{pmatrix}$$

Each number or letter is called an *element* of the matrix.

Addition of matrices

Matrices can be added, if they have the same *order*, by adding corresponding elements.

Example:

$$\begin{pmatrix} 2 & 3 & 1 \\ 0 & 4 & 0 \end{pmatrix} + \begin{pmatrix} 7. & 1 & 1 \\ 1 & 0 & 0 \end{pmatrix} = \begin{pmatrix} 9 & 4 & 2 \\ 1 & 4 & 0 \end{pmatrix}$$

Multiplication of matrices

Two matrices **A** and **B** can be multiplied if the number of elements in the *columns* of **A** equals the number of elements in the *rows* of **B**.

To form the *product* **AB** the orders of the matrices **A** and **B** must fit the pattern

$$\underset{p \text{ by } q}{\textbf{A}} \qquad \underset{q \text{ by } r}{\textbf{B}} \quad = \quad \underset{p \text{ by } r}{\textbf{AB}}$$

When we multiply two matrices **A** and **B**, we combine each row of **A** with each column of **B**.

Example:

If $\textbf{A} = \begin{pmatrix} 3 & 0 & 4 \\ 2 & 1 & 1 \end{pmatrix}$

2 by 3

and $\textbf{B} = \begin{pmatrix} 1 & 1 \\ 3 & 1 \\ 2 & 5 \end{pmatrix}$

3 by 2

then $\textbf{AB} = \begin{pmatrix} 3 & 0 & 4 \\ 2 & 1 & 1 \end{pmatrix} \begin{pmatrix} 1 & 1 \\ 3 & 1 \\ 2 & 5 \end{pmatrix}$

$$= \begin{pmatrix} 3 \times 1 + 0 \times 3 + 4 \times 2 & 3 \times 1 + 0 \times 1 + 4 \times 5 \\ 2 \times 1 + 1 \times 3 + 1 \times 2 & 2 \times 1 + 1 \times 1 + 1 \times 5 \end{pmatrix}$$

2 by 2

the first row of **A** combines with the first column of **B**

to give $(3 \quad 0 \quad 4) \begin{pmatrix} 1 \\ 3 \\ 2 \end{pmatrix} = 3 + 0 + 8 = 11$.

Combining the other rows and columns in a similar way

gives $\textbf{AB} = \begin{pmatrix} 11 & 23 \\ 7 & 8 \end{pmatrix}$

In this example it would also be possible to compute
BA to obtain $\begin{pmatrix} 5 & 1 & 5 \\ 11 & 1 & 13 \\ 16 & 5 & 13 \end{pmatrix}$

NOTE: In general, matrix multiplication is NOT *commutative*. If it is possible to form the product **BA** as well as **AB** then usually **BA** $\neq$ **AB**

For the *identity* and *inverse* of 2 by 2 matrices under multiplication, see **Identity Elements** and **Inverse Elements**

Matrix transformation

Matrices can be used to represent *transformations* of the *plane*. When (x, y) is an *object* point and (x′, y′) is the *image* point, then a matrix *equation* of the form

$$\begin{pmatrix} x' \\ y' \end{pmatrix} = \begin{pmatrix} a & b \\ c & d \end{pmatrix} \begin{pmatrix} x \\ y \end{pmatrix}$$

can be used to represent transformations such as *reflections*, *shears*, and *enlargements*.

Examples:

$$\begin{pmatrix} x' \\ y' \end{pmatrix} = \begin{pmatrix} 0 & ^-1 \\ 1 & 0 \end{pmatrix} \begin{pmatrix} x \\ y \end{pmatrix}$$

represents a $^+90°$ *rotation* about the *origin*

$$\begin{pmatrix} x' \\ y' \end{pmatrix} = \begin{pmatrix} 5 & 8 \\ ^-2 & ^-3 \end{pmatrix} \begin{pmatrix} x \\ y \end{pmatrix}$$

represents a shear with *invariant* line $y = {}^-\frac{1}{2}x$.

Mean

(More correctly its full name is Arithmetic Mean)
The mean is often just called the average by most non-mathematicians.
The mean of a *set* of n numbers is the *sum* of the n numbers divided by n.

Example: The mean of 1, 4, 3, 0, 1, 2, 1, 4 (eight numbers)

$$\text{is } (1 + 4 + 3 + 0 + 1 + 2 + 1 + 4) \div 8$$
$$= 16 \div 8$$
$$= 2$$

2 is the mean

Median

median height

The median of a *set* of numbers is the middle number once the numbers have been arranged in order of size.

Examples:
a) The median of   2, 0, 3, 1, 4, 1, 5, 3, 2
   is found from   0, 1, 1, 2, 2, 3, 3, 4, 5
                            ↓
                   2 is the median

b) The median of   1, 4, 3, 0, 1, 2, 1, 4
   is found from   0, 1, 1, 1, 2, 3, 4, 4
                            ↓

There are two middle values so $1\frac{1}{2}$ is the median

NOTE: For a large collection of *data*, the median is the value for which half the data is greater and half the data is less. In this case, the data is usually found from a *cumulative frequency* curve.

See Quartiles

61

Median of a triangle

A median of a triangle is the line drawn from a *vertex* of the *triangle* to the mid-point of the side opposite the vertex.

Examples:

There are three *medians* for every triangle, one from each vertex, and all of them pass through the same point.

---

mediator of
line segment
AB

Mediator

The mediator of a *line segment* AB is the line which cuts AB in half at *right-angles*.

The mediator is also the *line of symmetry* for the line segment.

Examples:

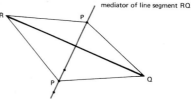

NOTE: The *locus* of points P which are equidistant from R and Q is the mediator of RQ.

See **Bisector**

Member

The *elements* of a *set* are said to be members of the set.
The *symbol* for 'is a member of' is ∈

Examples:

Pig is a member of the set of animals
Pig ∈ {animals}

5 is a member of the set of counting numbers.
$5 ∈ \{1, 2, 3, 4, 5, 6, 7, 8, \ldots\}$

Metre

The metre is the standard *unit* of length. We shorten metre to m

2 m

Example: A door is about 2 metres high.

Millimetre

A millimetre is one thousandth of a *metre*. We shorten millimetre to mm

$$1\,\text{mm} = \frac{1}{1000}\,\text{m}$$

This gap is one millimetre

Mixed number

A mixed number is a number which is a *whole number* with a *fraction*.

Examples:
$3\frac{1}{2}$, $2\frac{1}{5}$, $7\frac{3}{10}$, $4\frac{3}{5}$, $18\frac{3}{4}$,

NOTE: $3\frac{1}{2}$ is the *sum* $3 + \frac{1}{2}$

See **Improper Fraction**

Mode

The mode is the 'most popular' value, or the most frequently occurring item.

Example:
For   6, 7, 7, 8, 6, 5, 9, 8, 7, 6,
        5, 9, 8, 7, 4, 7, 8, 6, 8, 7,
        8, 5, 7, 7, 3, 7, 7, 3,

There are two 3's
There is one 4
There are three 5's
There are four 6's
There are ten 7's   7 comes TEN times.
There are six 8's
There are two 9's

7 is the mode, it comes most often.

NOTE: If there are TEN 7's and TEN 8's, then both 7 and 8 are modes.

Motif

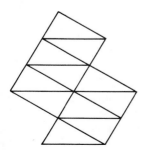

A motif is a small figure or shape that is repeated.

Example (left):
In this *tessellation*, the motif is

In a *pictogram* the motif is often or something else suitable.

Multiple

A multiple of a number n is k × n where k is a *counting number*.

Examples:
Some multiples of 4 are 8, 12, 20, 24, 28
Some multiples of 5 are 5, 15, 20, 25, 35
{multiples of 3} = {3, 6, 9, 12, 15, 18, 21, 24, ...}
{multiples of 7} = {7, 14, 21, 28, 35, 42, ...}

Multiplicative inverse

A multiplicative inverse is an *inverse* under multiplication.

Examples:

For numbers:
The multiplicative inverse of 3 is $\frac{1}{3}$ because $3 \times \frac{1}{3} = 1$
The multiplicative inverse of $\frac{1}{2}$ is 2 because $\frac{1}{2} \times 2 = 1$
The multiplicative inverse of $^-4$ is $^-\frac{1}{4}$ because $^-4 \times {}^-\frac{1}{4} = 1$
and 1 is the *identity* for numbers under multiplication.

For 2 by 2 matrices:
The multiplicative inverse of $\begin{pmatrix} 2 & 7 \\ 1 & 4 \end{pmatrix}$ is $\begin{pmatrix} 4 & ^-7 \\ ^-1 & 2 \end{pmatrix}$

because $\begin{pmatrix} 2 & 7 \\ 1 & 4 \end{pmatrix}\begin{pmatrix} 4 & ^-7 \\ ^-1 & 2 \end{pmatrix} = \begin{pmatrix} 1 & 0 \\ 0 & 1 \end{pmatrix}$ and $\begin{pmatrix} 1 & 0 \\ 0 & 1 \end{pmatrix}$

is the identity for 2 by 2 matrices under multiplication.

See **Inverse Elements**

Natural numbers

The *set* of natural numbers is another name for the set of *counting numbers*.
The set of natural numbers is {1, 2, 3, 4, 5, 6, 7...}
The set of counting numbers is usually represented by the *symbol* N, and is a *subset* of the set of *integers*. See **Whole Numbers**

Negative numbers

Negative numbers are used to count or measure in the opposite sense to the *positive numbers*. They are marked with a $^-$ sign.
{negative *integers*} = {$^-1$, $^-2$, $^-3$, $^-4$, $^-5$, $^-6$, $^-7$, $^-8$...}

See **Directed Numbers**

Example: Point A is 3 above *zero* and is a positive number
Point B is 3 below zero and is a negative number, $^-3$

NOTE: Negative numbers enable us to find an *additive inverse* for all *real numbers*.

Net

The net of a solid is the *plane shape*, which when cut out and folded, can be made into the solid shape.

Example: The shape shown in red can be cut out and made into the *cube*. It is one possible net for a cube.

Network

A network is any diagram of connected lines.

Examples:

In any network the three main features are:
the lines of the diagram—called *arcs*
the points at which the lines meet—called *nodes*
the areas for which the lines form a *boundary*—called *regions*.

See **Euler's Formula, Incidence Matrix, Route Matrix**

Node

A node is the point at the beginning and end of every *arc*. There must be a node where arcs meet on a *network*.

Examples:

P, Q, R, S, T, U, V, W and X are nodes.
See **Order of a Node**

Nonagon

A nonagon is a *polygon* bounded by 9 straight lines and containing 9 *angles*.

Examples:

This is a *regular* nonagon.

Nought

Nought is the *symbol*, 0, that stands for *zero*.

Null set

The null set is another name for the *empty set*. It is the *set* which has NO *members* and the symbol for it is ø, or { }.

Numerator   see **Fraction**

Object

In a *transformation* the shape or point being transformed is called the object.

Example:

• 0

If the *triangle* ABC is *rotated* ⁻90° about 0, the result is triangle A′B′C′.

The shape ABC, shown in red, is called the object; and the point A is an object point, for which A′ is its *image*.

See Image

In a *mapping* any number in the *set* being mapped is an object, but the whole set being mapped is usually called the *domain*.

Obtuse angle

An obtuse angle is an *angle* more than 90° but less than 180°.

Examples:

Octagon

An octagon is a *polygon* bounded by 8 straight lines and containing 8 *angles*.

Examples:

This is a *regular* octagon.

Octahedron

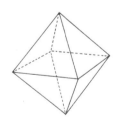

An octahedron is a solid shape with eight *faces*. In a *regular* octahedron each face is an *equilateral triangle*.

Example:

This is a regular octahedron.

Odd numbers

Odd numbers are *counting numbers* that are not *even*. Odd numbers do not divide exactly by 2. Odd numbers are those ending in 1 or 3 or 5 or 7 or 9

Examples: These are odd numbers:

7, 13, 21, 39, 403, 60827, 74155, 200461.

Operation

An operation is a way of combining *elements* in a *set*. The commonest kind of operation is a binary operation (binary meaning two). A binary operation combines two elements into one element.

Examples:

$\times$ is a binary operation on numbers
$$4 \times 2 = 8 \qquad \tfrac{1}{2} \times 6 = 3 \qquad 1 \times 9 = 9 \qquad 3 \times \tfrac{1}{3} = 1$$

$+$ is a binary operation on numbers
$$2 + 3 = 5 \qquad 1 + 7 = 8 \qquad 0 + 9 = 9 \qquad {}^{-}3 + 3 = 0$$

$\cup$ is a binary operation on sets
$$A \cup B = C \qquad A \cup C = D \qquad A \cup \emptyset = A$$

$+$ is a binary operation on *vectors*

$$\begin{pmatrix} 2 \\ 3 \end{pmatrix} + \begin{pmatrix} 5 \\ 1 \end{pmatrix} = \begin{pmatrix} 7 \\ 4 \end{pmatrix} \qquad\qquad \begin{pmatrix} 0 \\ 1 \end{pmatrix} + \begin{pmatrix} 5 \\ -6 \end{pmatrix} = \begin{pmatrix} 5 \\ -5 \end{pmatrix}$$

$$\begin{pmatrix} 0 \\ 0 \end{pmatrix} + \begin{pmatrix} 7 \\ 9 \end{pmatrix} = \begin{pmatrix} 7 \\ 9 \end{pmatrix}$$

multiplication is a binary operation on *matrices*

$$\begin{pmatrix} 1 & 1 \\ 2 & 3 \end{pmatrix}\begin{pmatrix} 4 & 1 \\ 0 & 2 \end{pmatrix} = \begin{pmatrix} 4 & 3 \\ 8 & 8 \end{pmatrix} \qquad\qquad \begin{pmatrix} 1 & 0 \\ 0 & 1 \end{pmatrix}\begin{pmatrix} 2 & 1 \\ 3 & 4 \end{pmatrix} = \begin{pmatrix} 2 & 1 \\ 3 & 4 \end{pmatrix}$$

See **Structure**

Order of a matrix

The order of a matrix is the size of the *matrix*. If a matrix has m *rows* and n *columns*, then the matrix is of order m by n.

Examples:

A matrix of order 2 by 3 is this size $\begin{pmatrix} \square & \square & \square \\ \square & \square & \square \end{pmatrix}$

If $A = \begin{pmatrix} 1 & 0 & 5 & 1 \\ 3 & 1 & 6 & 1 \\ 9 & 0 & 0 & 1 \end{pmatrix}$, then **A** is a 3 by 4 matrix.

If $B = (7 \quad 8 \quad 1 \quad 5 \quad 0)$, then **B** is a 1 by 5 matrix.

Order of a node

The order of a *node* is the number of *arcs* that meet at the node. The order of a node can be found by counting the number of paths leaving the node.

Examples:

A is a 3-node   D is a 1-node
B is a 4-node   E is a 5-node
C is a 3-node   F is a 2-node

NOTE: We usually ignore all 2-nodes such as F.

Order of rotational
symmetry see **Rotational Symmetry**

Ordered pairs

When we use pairs of numbers and the order is important they are called ordered pairs.

Examples:
Coordinates are ordered pairs: (2, 3) is not the same point as (3, 2)
The order 2, 3 matters.

The ordered pair (1, 4) is a *solution* to the *equation*
y = x + 3 because $\boxed{4} = \boxed{1} + 3$ but (4, 1) is not a solution
$\boxed{1} \neq \boxed{4} + 3$; the order 1, 4 matters.

Origin

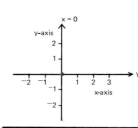

The origin is the point with *coordinates* (0, 0).
It is the point where the *axes* cross. It is the point where the line x = 0 and the line y = 0 *intersect*.

The origin is the point shown by the red dot.

Parabola

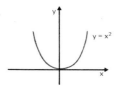

This is the shape obtained by plotting the *function* $x \rightarrow x^2$ using *coordinates*. It is also the shape for any function of the form
$x \rightarrow ax^2 + bx + c$.
It is a familiar shape for it is approximately the path followed by a ball in flight; the shape of the wires supporting a suspension bridge; the cross section of the reflector for an electric bar fire.

Examples:

Parallel

Lines are parallel if they NEVER meet, no matter how far they are extended.

Examples: A pair of railway lines are parallel.

Parallel lines are always the same distance apart and they never *intersect*. Arrows are used to show parallel lines, as shown on the left.

Parallelogram

A parallelogram is a *quadrilateral* formed by two pairs of *parallel* lines. It has:

a) NO *lines of symmetry*;
b) *rotational symmetry* of order 2;
c) opposite sides equal;
d) opposite *angles* of the figure equal;
e) *diagonals bisecting* each other.

Examples (left and right):

Pascal's triangle

Pascal's triangle is a pattern of numbers. The triangle pattern starts with and the general rule for continuing the pattern is—'add each pair of numbers and write the result underneath; putting 1 at the beginning and 1 at the end.'

```
                          1
                      1       1
                  1       2       1
              1       3       3       1
          1       4       6       4       1
      1    1+4     4+6    10      5       1
    1       6      15     20    10+5     6       1
  1       7       21     35     35      21      7       1
  *       *       *       *       *       *       *     *   *
*     *     *     *     *     *     *     *     *     *
```

Pattern lines

Pattern lines are the lines used to draw an *enlargement*. They go through the centre of enlargement and *corresponding points* in the shapes.

Example:

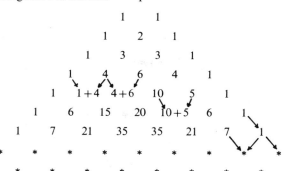

These are the pattern lines, shown in red.

centre of enlargement

Pentagon

A pentagon is a *polygon* bounded by 5 straight lines and containing 5 *angles*.

Examples:

This is a *regular* pentagon.

Percentage

A percentage is a *fraction*. It is another way of writing a *percentage fraction*.

Examples: $\dfrac{20}{100} = 20\%$ $\dfrac{83}{100} = 83\%$ $\dfrac{22\frac{1}{2}}{100} = 22\frac{1}{2}\%$.

NOTE: % is 100 rewritten in a special way.

Percentage fraction

A percentage fraction is a *fraction* with a *denominator* of 100.

Examples:

$$\frac{3}{100}, \frac{25}{100}, \frac{97}{100}, \frac{117}{100}, \frac{42\frac{1}{2}}{100}, \frac{350}{100},$$

By means of *equivalent fractions*, any fraction can be written as a percentage fraction and as a *percentage*.

Examples:

$$\frac{1}{4} = \frac{1 \times 25}{4 \times 25} = \frac{25}{100} = 25\% \qquad \frac{3}{8} = \frac{3 \times 12\frac{1}{2}}{8 \times 12\frac{1}{2}} = \frac{37\frac{1}{2}}{100} = 37\frac{1}{2}\%$$

$$\frac{2}{3} = \frac{2 \times 33\frac{1}{3}}{3 \times 33\frac{1}{3}} = \frac{66\frac{2}{3}}{100} = 66\frac{2}{3}\%.$$

Perfect number

A perfect number is a *counting number* which equals the *sum* of all its *factors* except itself.

Examples:
6   {factors of 6} = {1, 2, 3, 6}
                       1 + 2 + 3 = 6
28   {factors of 28} = {1, 2, 4, 7, 14, 28}
                       1 + 2 + 4 + 7 + 14 = 28

NOTE: After 6 and 28 the next perfect number is 496.

Perimeter

The perimeter or a figure (or shape) is the length of the *boundary* or the distance around the outside of the shape.

Example (left):
Perimeter is 3 + 3 + 3 + 3 + 3 + 4 + 8 = 27

Perpendicular

Lines are perpendicular if they cross at *right-angles*.

Examples:

Similarly *planes* are perpendicular if they meet at right-angles. For example, in most rooms a wall and a floor are perpendicular.

Pi

Pi (or π) is the *ratio* of the *circumference* of a *circle* to its *diameter*. For ALL circles the *fraction*

$$\frac{\text{circumference}}{\text{diameter}} \text{ is } \pi \qquad \text{or} \qquad C = \pi d$$

Pi is also used in calculating the *area* inside a circle. $A = \pi r^2$

π is approximately
$= 3$ (1 *significant figure*)
$= 3.1$ (2 significant figures)
$= 3.14$ (3 significant figures)
another good approximation for π is $3\frac{1}{7}$ or $\frac{22}{7}$

$\pi = 3.141\ 592\ 653\ 589\ 79\ldots$

Pi is an *irrational* number.

Examples:
The distance around a circular pond that is 1 km across is
$C = \pi \times d$
$= 3 \times 1$
$= 3$ km (1 S.F.)

The area of a circular mirror with radius 40 cm is
$A = \pi \times r^2$
$= \pi \times 40^2$
$= 3.142 \times 1600$
$= 50.3$ cm^2 (3 S.F.)

Pictogram

A pictogram is a way of representing information. It is a kind of *graph* used in statistics. It is similar to a *bar chart*, but made using a *motif*.

Example (right):
Pictogram showing how pupils in form 1B come to school.

represents 1 pupil

walk	🚶🚶🚶🚶🚶🚶🚶🚶🚶🚶🚶
bus	🚶🚶🚶🚶
cycle	🚶🚶🚶🚶🚶

Pie chart

A pie chart is a way of representing information. It is a kind of *graph* used in statistics.

Example (left):
Pie chart showing how Jimmy Smith spent last Saturday.
15° represent 1 hour

NOTE: The *circle* is divided into *sectors* so that the *areas* of the *sectors* represent the *data*.

73

Plane

A *plane* is a flat surface like a table-top.
A plane has no thickness and extends forever into space in all directions.

Example (left): When slicing a loaf of bread, the knife must be kept in one plane in order to get flat slices.

Plane shape

A plane shape is a shape that can be drawn with all its points in one *plane*.

Examples: All *polygons*, such as *squares* and *triangles*, are plane shapes, as are *circles*.

Plane of symmetry

A solid has a plane of symetry if there is a *plane* which can act as a mirror to show the complete shape.

Examples (left and right):
For each solid the
plane of symmetry
is shown in red.

Point symmetry

A solid (or shape) has point *symmetry* if it can be given an *enlargement* with *scale factor* $^-1$ about one point so that the *image* occupies the same position as the *object*.

Examples:

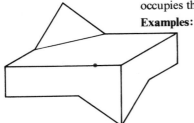

This solid has
point symmetry
about the red dot.

This *plane shape* has
point symmetry
about the red dot.

'A plane shape has point symmetry' is equivalent to saying that it has *rotational symmetry* of *order* 2.

Polar coordinates

See **Coordinates** for Cartesian coordinates.
Polar coordinates are another way of describing the position of

points in a *plane*. Instead of (x, y), the distance r from the *origin* and the *angle* θ from a fixed direction are given. The position of a point P is then given by (r, θ) in polar coordinates. (*Anticlockwise* angles are indicated by *positive numbers*.)

Examples:

A is (2,30°)   B is (1,90°)
C is (3,150°)   D is (2,270°)

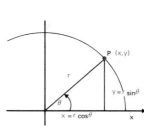

If P is (x, y) in Cartesian coordinates and if P is (r, θ) in polar coordinates then

$$x = r \cos \theta, \quad y = r \sin \theta$$

and $$r = \sqrt{x^2 + y^2}, \quad \tan \theta = \frac{x}{y}$$

Polygon

A polygon is a *plane shape* bounded by only straight lines.

Examples:

3 sides   triangle

4 sides   quadrilateral

5 sides   pentagon

6 sides   hexagon

7 sides   heptagon

8 sides   octagon

75

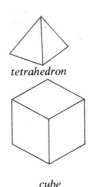
tetrahedron

Polyhedron (plural **Polyhedra**)

A polyhedron is a solid shape with flat sides. The flat sides or *faces* are all *polygons*.

Examples: See **Cube, Cuboid, Dodecahedron, Icosahedron, Octahedron, Prism, Pyramid, Rectangular Prism, Tetrahedron.**

NOTE: There are only these five *regular* polyhedra:

cube   *octahedron*   *dodecahedron*   *icosahedron*

Positive numbers

Positive numbers are numbers greater than *zero* such as
3,   2.56,   0.00081
On the number line any number to the right of zero (as shown by the red line) is a positive number.

Positive *integers* work like the *counting numbers* and so we do not always use the $^+$ sign.
$\{^+1, {}^+2, {}^+3, {}^+4, {}^+5 \ldots\} = \{1, 2, 3, 4, 5 \ldots\}$

See **Negative Numbers**

Power of a number

The power of a number is the result of a multiplication using just that number.

Examples:

$\left. \begin{array}{l} 2 \times 2 \times 2 = 8 \\ 2 \times 2 \times 2 \times 2 \times 2 = 32 \\ 2 \times 2 = 4 \end{array} \right\}$ 8, 32 and 4 are some powers of 2

2 to the power 3 is $2 \times 2 \times 2$ and is written as 2^3
2 to the power 5 is $2 \times 2 \times 2 \times 2 \times 2$ and is written as 2^5

Similarly
$2^{10} = 2 \times 2 \times 2 \times 2 \times 2 \times 2 \times 2 \times 2 \times 2 \times 2 = 1024$
$3^4 = 3 \times 3 \times 3 \times 3 = 81$
$5^3 = 5 \times 5 \times 5 = 125$

NOTE: A number 'to the power 2' is said to be '*squared*'.

7^2 is 7 squared
$\qquad = 7 \times 7$
$\qquad = 49$
It is equal to the *area* of a *square* of side 7.

A number 'to the power 3' is said to be *'cubed'*
3^3 is 3 cubed
$$= 3 \times 3 \times 3$$
$$= 27$$
It is equal to the *volume* of a *cube* of side 3.

Prime factors

Prime factors of a number are *factors* of the number which are also *prime numbers*.

Example:
{factors of 24} = {1, 2, 3, 4, 6, 8, 12, 24}
                       prime numbers
{prime factors of 24} = {2, 3}

NOTE: We can write any number as a *product* of prime factors.

Examples:

$18 = 2 \times 3 \times 3$ $60 = 2 \times 2 \times 3 \times 5$

Prime number

A prime number has only two *factors*, itself and 1.

Examples:
$17 = 17 \times 1$ $13 = 13 \times 1$
17 and 13 cannot be written as *products* of any other *counting numbers*.

{prime numbers} = {2, 3, 5, 7, 11, 13, 17, 19, 23, 29, 31, 37, 41, 43...}
A prime number is a number that is not a *rectangle number*.

NOTE: The number 1 is not a prime number and it is not a rectangle number.

Prism

A prism is a *polyhedron* with the same shape along its length.

Examples:

Probability

Probability is a measure of how likely an event is. The probability of an event is a number between 0 and 1.

Examples:
Probability of a man having two heads is 0
Probability of rolling a three with one die is $\frac{1}{6}$ or 0.16666...
Probability of a newborn baby being a boy is $\frac{1}{2}$ or 0.5
Probability of not picking a spade from a new pack of cards is $\frac{3}{4}$
Probability of you dying in the next 200 years is 1

Mathematically,

$$\text{probability of an event} \quad S = \frac{\text{number of ways S can happen}}{\text{number of possible outcomes}}$$

provided that the possible outcomes are all *equally likely*.

Example (left):
S = {a total score of seven when two dice are rolled}
P = {all possible number pairs when two dice are rolled}
S = {(1, 6), (2, 5), (3, 4), (4, 3), (5, 2), (6, 1)}
number in S is 6
P = {all 36 points on the graph}
number in P is 36
so, the probability of scoring seven when two dice are rolled is $\frac{6}{36}$
$= \frac{1}{6}$

Product

The product of two or more numbers is the result of multiplying them together.

Examples:
The product of 6 and 7 is $6 \times 7 = 42$
The product of 2 and 5 is $2 \times 5 = 10$
The same word is used for the result of multiplying two *matrices* together.

Proportion

Two quantities are in proportion when corresponding pairs are always in the same *ratio*.

Example: The number of pens, n, bought in a shop at a cost of C pence, is shown in this table:

Number of pens, n	1	2	3	4	5	10	20
Cost of pens, C	2	4	6	8	10	20	40

The ratios 2 to 4, 5 to 10, 20 to 40, etc. are equal, so the quantities n and C are in proportion.

Pyramid

A pyramid is a *polyhedron* with a *polygon* for a base and all other *faces* meeting at one *vertex* called the apex.

Examples: The bases are shaded red and some apexes are shown by a red dot.

These two on the left are *square*-based pyramids

This is a *triangular*-based pyramid, it is the same solid as a *tetrahedron*.

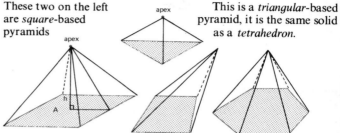

The *volume* of ANY pyramid is given by

volume = $\frac{1}{3}$ × base area × *perpendicular* height of the apex above the base

$$V = \tfrac{1}{3}Ah$$

Pythagoras

Pythagoras' rule says that in a *right-angled triangle*, the *area* of a *square* on the longest side is equal to the *sum* of the areas of squares drawn on the two smaller sides.

Area A = Area B + Area C

OR

$$p^2 = q^2 + r^2$$

Examples:

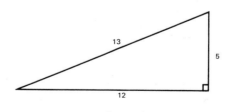

A = B + C
25 = 9 + 16
OR
$5^2 = 3^2 + 4^2$

$13^2 = 12^2 + 5^2$
$169 = 144 + 25$

Some *sets* of three numbers that fit this pattern are

{3, 4, 5}   {5, 12, 13}   {8, 15, 17}
{7, 24, 25}   {20, 21, 29}   {12, 35, 37}

Quadratic equation

A quadratic equation in x is an *equation* involving x to the *power* 2 but no higher powers of x.
The general form of a quadratic equation is
$ax^2 + bx + c = 0$

Examples:
$3x^2 = 12$ $x^2 + 1 = 26$ $x^2 - 2x + 1 = 0$

When a quadratic equation has *solutions* and the equation is written in the general form, the solutions can be found using the *formula*

$$x = \frac{-b \pm \sqrt{b^2 - 4ac}}{2a}$$

Quadratic relation

A quadratic relation is a *relation* of the form
$x \rightarrow ax^2 + bx + c$ where $a \neq 0$

Examples:
$x \rightarrow 2x^2$
$x \rightarrow x^2 + 3$
$x \rightarrow 5x^2 + x - 13$
$x \rightarrow 9 - x^2$

Quadrilateral

A quadrilateral is a *plane shape* with four straight sides.

Examples:

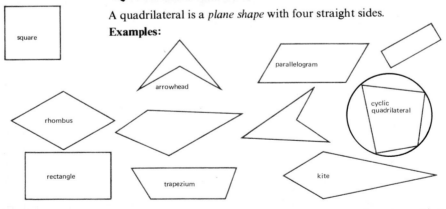

square

arrowhead

parallelogram

cyclic quadrilateral

rhombus

rectangle

trapezium

kite

Quartile

When there is a large amount of *data* some idea of its spread is given by the quartiles. These are the values for which $\frac{1}{4}$ or $\frac{1}{2}$ or $\frac{3}{4}$ of the data is less. We usually use a *cumulative frequency* diagram to find the quartiles.

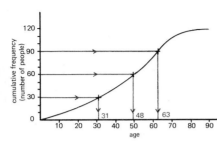

Example (left): In a village 120 people are asked their age. The first quartile is 31 years because $\frac{1}{4}$ of the people are 31 years or less.
The second quartile is 48 years because $\frac{1}{2}$ of the people are 48 years or less.
The third quartile is 63 years because $\frac{3}{4}$ of the people are 63 years or less.
The second quartile is the same as the *median*.

Quotient

The quotient is the result you get when you do a division.

Example:

In the division $6\overline{)4218}$ with quotient 703, 703 is the quotient.

Radius

The radius of a *circle* is the distance from the centre of the circle to a point on the circle.

Example (left):
All the points on the circle C are 2 cm from the centre P.

Range

First meaning

(*Mappings*). The range of a *function* is the *set* of numbers onto which the *domain* is *mapped*. The range is the same as the *image* set.

Example (left):
$\{2, 4, 6, 8, 10\}$ is the domain $\{2, 3, 4, 5, 6\}$ is the range.

Second meaning

(Statistics). In a collection of *data*, the range is the *difference* between the highest and the lowest values.

Example:

135 children took an examination; the lowest mark was 11 and the highest mark was 91.
The range is $91 - 11 = 80$ marks

Ratio

A ratio is used to compare two or more quantities.

Examples:
A youth club has 30 boy members and 40 girl members.
    The ratio of boys to girls is 30 to 40
A football team has won 17 matches and lost 10 matches.
    The ratio of wins to losses is 17 to 10

With each ratio we think of a *fraction* that goes with it.

Examples:
The ratio 5 to 7 and the fraction $\frac{5}{7}$
The ratio 15 to 20 and the fraction $\frac{15}{20}$ or $\frac{3}{4}$
NOTE: Ratios are equal when their fractions are *equivalent*.

LEAGUE TABLE	Won	Lost
Chelsea	5	11
Newcastle	20	6
Leeds	17	10
West Ham	14	14
Ipswich	12	19

Rational numbers

A rational number is one that can be written as a *fraction*.

The *set* of rationals is $\left\{ \dfrac{p}{q} \right.$ such that p and q are *integers*,

$q \neq 0$, and p and q have no common *factor* $\left. \right\}$.

Examples: $\frac{2}{3}$, $\frac{-7}{8}$, $\frac{15}{19}$, $\frac{8}{1}$, $\frac{1}{13}$, $\frac{-42}{5}$ are examples of rational numbers
See **Irrational**

The set of rational numbers is a *subset* of the set of *real numbers*.

The set of integers is a subset of the set of rational numbers.

NOTE: A rational number can always be written as a decimal that either *terminates* or *recurs*.

Real number

The *set* of real numbers is the set of ALL numbers that can be written as a decimal.
The set of real numbers is the *union* of the set of *rational* numbers and the set of *irrational* numbers.

See **Continuous**

NOTE: An example of a number that is NOT real is $\sqrt{-1}$. Numbers such as $\sqrt{-1}$, $\sqrt{-7}$, and $\sqrt{-16}$ are called complex numbers.

Reciprocal

The reciprocal of a number x, is the number $\frac{1}{x}$

Examples:

The reciprocal of 2 is $\frac{1}{2}$

The reciprocal of 8 is $\frac{1}{8}$

The reciprocal of $\frac{1}{3}$ is 3

The reciprocal of $\frac{4}{7}$ is $\frac{7}{4}$

The reciprocal of $\frac{10}{3}$ is $\frac{3}{10}$

The reciprocal of a number is the same as the *multiplicative inverse* of the number.

Rectangle

A rectangle is a *quadrilateral* formed by two pairs of *parallel* lines crossing at *right-angles*.

Examples:

See **Square**

A rectangle has:

a) two *lines of symmetry*;

b) *rotational symmetry* of *order* 2;

c) opposite sides equal;

d) all four *angles* of the figure equal to 90°;

e) *diagonals* equal and *bisecting* each other.

Rectangle number

A rectangle number is a number that can be shown as a pattern of dots in the shape of a *rectangle*.

Examples:

6 = 2 × 3
. . .
. . .

16 = 4 × 4 or
. . . .
. . . .
. . . .
. . . .

16 = 2 × 8
. . . .
. . . .

21 = 3 × 7
. . . .
. . . .
. . . .

{rectangle numbers} = {4, 6, 8, 9, 10, 12, 14, 15, 16, 18,...}

See **Prime Number** and **Square Number**

NOTE: The number 1 is not a rectangle number and it is not a *prime number*.

Rectangular prism

A rectangular prism is a *prism* with the shape of a *rectangle* along its length. **See Cuboid**

Recurring decimal

A recurring decimal has one *digit*, or a group of digits, that is repeated endlessly.

Examples:

$\frac{1}{3} = 0.333333\ldots$ $\frac{6}{11} = 0.545454\ldots$

$\frac{1}{7} = 0.142857142857142857\ldots$

We shorten these answers like this:

$\frac{1}{3} = 0.\dot{3}$ $\frac{6}{11} = 0.\dot{5}\dot{4}$ $\frac{1}{7} = 0.\dot{1}4285\dot{7}$

NOTE: 0.404004000400004000004000000004...
has a kind of repeating pattern but it is NOT a recurring decimal (it is an *irrational number*).

Re-entrant

A *polygon* which is not *convex* is said to be re-entrant.

Examples:

The re-entrant part is shown in red.

In a re-entrant polygon, one of the *angles* of the polygon is *reflex*.

Reflection

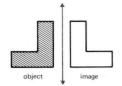

object   image

Reflection is a way of *transforming* a shape as a mirror does.
In a *plane*, the result of giving an *object* a reflection in a mirror
line, is called its mirror *image*.

Example (right):

If P and P′ are *corresponding points*
then the mirror line m is
a *mediator* of PP′.

Reflection matrices

Some of the simpler reflections that can be represented as a
2 by 2 *matrix* are

$$\begin{pmatrix} {}^-1 & 0 \\ 0 & 1 \end{pmatrix}$$

$x = 0$ as
mirror line

$$\begin{pmatrix} 1 & 0 \\ 0 & {}^-1 \end{pmatrix}$$

$y = 0$ as
mirror line

$$\begin{pmatrix} 0 & 1 \\ 1 & 0 \end{pmatrix}$$

$y = x$ as
mirror line

$$\begin{pmatrix} 0 & {}^-1 \\ {}^-1 & 0 \end{pmatrix}$$

$y = {}^-x$ as
mirror line

Reflex angle

A reflex angle is an *angle* that is more than 180° and less than
360°.

Examples:

85

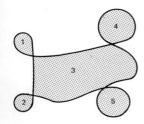

Region

A region is a part of a surface.

Regions in topology
In *topology* a region is a space bounded by *arcs*.

Example:
In this *network* there are SIX regions. Five of the six regions are shaded red and the space surrounding the network is another region.

Regions on a graph
On a *graph* a straight line divides the *plane* into two regions.

Examples:

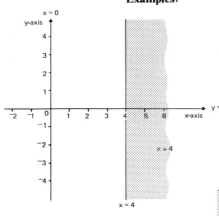

The straight line x = 4 (*left*) divides the plane into two regions. The points in the region shaded red are described by the *inequality* x > 4

The straight lines y = ⁻1 and y = 2 (*below*) divide the plane into three regions. The points in the region shaded red are described by the inequality ⁻1 < y < 2

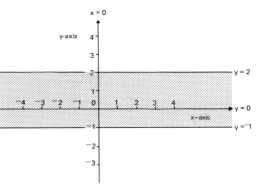

Regular

Regular polygon
A regular *polygon* has all its sides the same length and all its *angles* the same size.

Examples:

Regular polyhedron
A regular *polyhedron* is a polyhedron with *identical* regular polygons for all of its *faces*.

Relation

Relation in general
A relation is a way of connecting *sets* of things such as numbers or people.

Examples:
'——is the mother of——'
'——is a factor of——'
'——is 5 more than——'
'——is greater than——'

Relations can be shown by an *arrow diagram* or a *relation diagram* (there is no real difference between these two).

Relations which are mappings
A *mapping* is a special relation. See **Mapping**.
Most mathematical relations are mappings and are called either mappings or *functions*. See **Functions**.
The same mathematical relation can be shown in various ways.

Example: Here is just ONE relation but shown in six different ways:

This is a
mapping diagram.

This is a
relation diagram.

This is a set of *ordered pairs*
$\{(^-1, 1), (0, 2), (1, 3), (2, 4), (3, 5), (4, 6)\}$

This is a *graph*

$x \rightarrow x + 2$ This is a relation or mapping.

$y = x + 2$ This is an *equation.*

Relation diagram

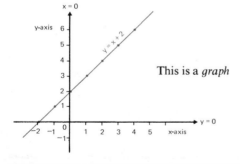

'——is a factor of——'

A relation diagram is similar to an *arrow diagram* and is used to show a *relation*.

Example:

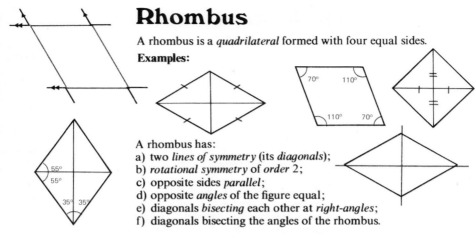

Rhombus

A rhombus is a *quadrilateral* formed with four equal sides.

Examples:

A rhombus has:
a) two *lines of symmetry* (its *diagonals*);
b) *rotational symmetry* of *order* 2;
c) opposite sides *parallel*;
d) opposite *angles* of the figure equal;
e) diagonals *bisecting* each other at *right-angles*;
f) diagonals bisecting the angles of the rhombus.

Right-angle

A right-angle is a quarter of a turn.

It is measured as an *angle* of 90°.

This very important angle is usually shown by a little box as illustrated in the diagram.

Examples:

Right-angled triangle

A right-angled triangle is a *triangle* with a *right-angle* for one of the three angles.

Examples:

A right-angled *isosceles* triangle also has two equal sides.

Examples:

See **Pythagoras**

Rotation

A rotation is a *transformation* in which every point turns through the same *angle* about the same centre. The *centre of* the *rotation* is the one point that is *invariant*.

Example: In this rotation each line a, b, and c has turned through an angle of 60° about the centre O.
A rotation of 60° about O gives the red P as the image of the black P.

Rotation matrices

Some of the simpler rotations that can be represented as a 2 by 2 *matrix* are those rotations about the *origin*.

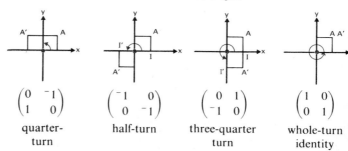

$$\begin{pmatrix} 0 & -1 \\ 1 & 0 \end{pmatrix} \qquad \begin{pmatrix} -1 & 0 \\ 0 & -1 \end{pmatrix} \qquad \begin{pmatrix} 0 & 1 \\ -1 & 0 \end{pmatrix} \qquad \begin{pmatrix} 1 & 0 \\ 0 & 1 \end{pmatrix}$$

quarter-turn   half-turn   three-quarter turn   whole-turn identity

The matrix equivalent to a rotation through an *angle* θ

is $\begin{pmatrix} \cos\theta & -\sin\theta \\ \sin\theta & \cos\theta \end{pmatrix}$

Rotational symmetry

A shape has rotational *symmetry* if, after a *rotation*, every *image* point is *mapped onto* the *object* shape.

Examples: The shape on the left has rotational symmetry. There are four rotations about O which will map each point of the shape onto itself.

A rotation of 90° about O will map, for example, A onto A'.
A rotation of 180° about O will map, for example, A onto A".
A rotation of 270° about O will map, for example, A onto A'''.
A rotation of 360° about O will map, for example, A onto A.

For this fan the red line is an *axis* of rotational symmetry. The solid shape can be rotated about the axis through 120°, or 240°, or 360°, mapping each point of a blade onto a point of another blade.

Order of rotational symmetry

The order of rotational symmetry for a shape is the number of possible rotations, that give rotational symmetry.

Examples:

For this shape the order of rotational symmetry is 4.

For this fan, the order of rotational symmetry is 3.

order of rotational symmetry is 1

order of rotational symmetry is 2

order of rotational symmetry is 3

Rounding off

Rounding off a number is a way of writing the number with fewer non-*zero digits.*

Examples:
£1.02 to the nearest pound is £1
£17.31 to the nearest pound is £17
£0.91 to the nearest pound is £1
308.5 to the nearest whole number is 309
0.612 to the nearest whole number is 1
0.498 to the nearest whole number is 0
13.77 to the nearest whole number is 14

When the first digit to be ignored, (shown in red), is a 5, 6, 7, 8, or 9 then we 'round up'; when it is a 0, 1, 2, 3, or 4 then we 'round down'.

Examples:
2392 to the nearest hundred is 2400 (rounded up)
2342 to the nearest hundred is 2300 (rounded down)
72849 to the nearest hundred is 72800 (rounded down)
106951 to the nearest hundred is 107000 (rounded up)
687 to the nearest ten is 690 (rounded up)
9619 to the nearest thousand is 10000 (rounded up)

Route matrix

In a *network*, a route matrix is a *matrix* showing the number of *arcs* connecting each pair of *nodes*.

Example: For the network below, the route matrix is **M**.

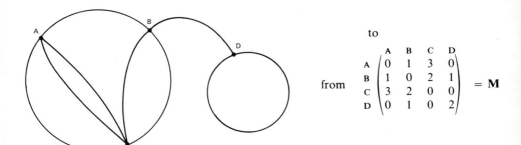

$$\text{from} \quad \begin{array}{c} \\ A \\ B \\ C \\ D \end{array} \begin{array}{c} \overset{\text{to}}{} \\ \begin{pmatrix} \overset{A}{0} & \overset{B}{1} & \overset{C}{3} & \overset{D}{0} \\ 1 & 0 & 2 & 1 \\ 3 & 2 & 0 & 0 \\ 0 & 1 & 0 & 2 \end{pmatrix} \end{array} = \mathbf{M}$$

Route matrix usually means *direct route* matrix.

NOTE: The direct route matrix could also be called the one-stage route matrix. A two-stage route matrix is for routes travelling along two arcs. For the above network the two-stage route matrix can be found by the matrix multiplication **M** × **M**.

See **Incidence Matrix**

Row

A list of numbers (or letters) across the page is called a row.
Coordinates are always written in a row.

Examples:
(3, 4),   (1, 9),   (‾7, ‾5)

When a *matrix* consists of only a row it is called a row matrix.

Example:
(4   2   8   0   ‾1)

Scale factor

When objects are *similar*, their sizes can be compared by looking
at the *ratio* of the lengths of their corresponding parts, e.g. the
handles of the saucepans.

Linear scale factor

The linear scale factor is the number of times the length on one
object is bigger than the corresponding length on the similar
object.

Example: The child's chair is made similar to the adult's chair
on a scale 1 to 2.

The scale factor for the child's chair from the adult's is $\frac{1}{2}$.

The scale factor for the adult's chair from the child's is 2.

Scale factor of enlargement

In an *enlargement* a scale factor is used to produce a similar shape.

Example: The enlargement P'Q'R' of shape PQR is made with centre O and scale factor 3.

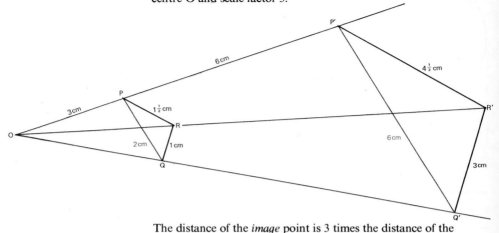

The distance of the *image* point is 3 times the distance of the *corresponding object* point from the centre of enlargement:

$$OP' = 3 \times OP \qquad OQ' = 3 \times OQ \qquad OR' = 3 \times OR$$

Also, the image lengths are three times the object lengths:

$$P'Q' = 3 \times PQ$$

We shorten 'scale factor' to S.F.

Area scale factor

The area scale factor is the number of times the *area* of one shape is bigger than the area of the similar shape.

Example (left):

The area P' is 9 times the area P, so the area scale factor is 9; but the linear scale factor is 3.

If the linear scale factor is k then the area scale factor is k^2.

See **Enlargement** (Enlargement Matrix)

Scalene triangle

A scalene triangle is a *triangle* whose sides are all of different lengths.

Examples:

NOTE: A scalene triangle can be *right-angled.*

Sector of a circle

A sector of a *circle* is a shape whose *boundary* is an *arc* of the circle and two *radii* of the circle. It is the shape of the top of a slice of cake or a wedge of cheese.

Examples:

Segment of a circle

The segment of a *circle* is a shape whose *boundary* is an *arc* of the circle and a *chord* of the circle.

Examples:

A chord normally divides a circle into two segments of different sizes. The smaller segment is called the minor segment and the larger segment is called the major segment.

Self inverse see Inverse Pair

Semicircle

Semicircle means half a *circle*. It is the shape formed by a *diameter* and the *arc* of the circle joining its endpoints.

Examples:

The *line segment* AB is always a diameter.

hockey pitch

basketball court

Semi-interquartile range

The semi-interquartile range is half the *interquartile range*.

Sense

If the order of the points A, B, C, D . . . on a shape is *clockwise*, and the order of the *corresponding points* A′, B′, C′, D′ . . . on a *congruent* shape is *anticlockwise* then the two shapes do NOT have the same sense.

Example:

These two shapes do NOT have the same sense.

An *object* and its *image* under a *reflection* (or a *glide reflection*) are always of opposite sense.

When a *transformation* can be represented by a *matrix* **M**, then the *determinant* of **M** shows the sense of the images. If det **M** is *negative* there is a change in sense, and if det **M** is *positive* then sense is an *invariant* property for the transformation.

Set

A set is any collection of things. The *members* of a set could be numbers, names, letters, shapes, *matrices*, etc.

Examples:
The set of vowels is {a, e, i, o, u}
The set of *whole numbers* less than 5 is {0, 1, 2, 3, 4}
{*even numbers*} = {2, 4, 6, 8, 10, 12, 14, 16, . . .}
{traffic-light colours} = {red, amber, green}

When we use some *elements* of a set A to form a new set, the new set is called a *subset* of A.

Example:
If A = {1, 3, 5, 7, 9} and B = {3, 5, 7} then
B is a subset of A.

When we put the elements of A and the elements of B into one set, this new set is called the *union* of A and B.

Example:
If A = {t, i, m} and B = {j, i, m} then {t, i, j, m} is the union of A and B.

NOTE: The order of the elements doesn't matter and we never put the same element in a set more than once.

When we take the elements that come in both set A and in set B, then the new set is called the *intersection* of A and B.

Example:
If A = {△, □, ○} and B = {△, □, +, *} then {△, □} is the intersection of A and B.

See **Complement of a Set, Empty Set, Universal Set**

Shear

A shear is a *transformation* in which all points slide *parallel* to a fixed line, or *plane*, keeping all straight lines straight.

Examples:

The black shape is the *object* and the red shape is the *image* after the shear.

The *areas* of the object shape and the image shape are the same.

Example:
The area of the black triangle is 10 and the area of the red triangle is 10.

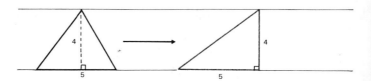

There is always an *invariant* line and all points move parallel to it. The invariant line need not be on the shape.

Example:
Line p is the invariant line for this shear.

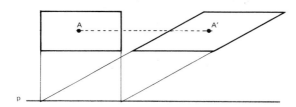

The line joining A and A' its image, is parallel to p.
The *ratio* of, the distance moved by points, to their distance from the invariant line, is constant.

Shear matrix
The transformation

$$\begin{pmatrix} x \\ y \end{pmatrix} \rightarrow \begin{pmatrix} 1 & 0 \\ k & 1 \end{pmatrix}\begin{pmatrix} x \\ y \end{pmatrix}$$

represents a shear with $x = 0$ invariant and the point $(1, 0)$ having the image $(1, k)$

Any *matrix* $\begin{pmatrix} a & b \\ c & d \end{pmatrix}$ where $a + d = 2$ and $ad - bc = 1$

will represent a shear.

Shift numbers

Shift numbers is another name for *directed numbers* or *integers*.

Examples: $^+3, ^+1, ^-7, ^-8, ^+2, ^-23$

Significant figures

The most significant figure (or *digit*) in a number, is the first digit (not *zero*) that you reach, reading left to right.

Examples:

The significant figures are shown in red.

7861

54002

91   Here, the ONE most significant
0.006103   figure is in red.
0.01007
3.09988

            Here, shown in red, are:
8140.09   the TWO most significant figures;
61954   the THREE most significant figures;
7089.3   the THREE most significant figures;
60 219   the FOUR most significant figures;
0.042871   the THREE most significant figures;
0.040000   the FOUR most significant figures.

When approximating to a given number of significant figures, we use *rounding off* on the last significant figure.

We shorten the words 'significant figures' to S.F. or sig. fig.

Similar

Two objects are similar if they are the same shape.

Examples:

 and are similar

 and are similar

With similar objects, all the lengths of one object are a fixed number of times the corresponding lengths of the other object. This number is called the *scale factor*.

Example:

All the lengths on the large box of Crispies are $1\frac{1}{2}$ times the corresponding lengths of the small box of Crispies.

With similar objects, corresponding *angles* are equal.

Example:

$$\frac{\triangle \text{XYZ}}{\triangle \text{X'Y'Z'}}$$ are similar

See **Enlargement**

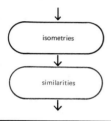

Similarities

Similarities are *transformations* in which *angles* are *invariant*.

Example: *Enlargements* are similarities.

Similarities come after the *isometries* in the hierarchy of transformations. Isometries preserve length, which similarities do not.

Simple closed curve

A closed curve is a line with the end point joined to the beginning.
A simple curve does not have one part crossing another.
A simple closed curve has both these properties.

Examples:

Any *topological transformation* of a *circle* is a simple closed curve.
Any simple closed curve can be transformed topologically into a circle.

Simultaneous equations

Simultaneous equations are *equations* that have the same *solution(s)*. The equations are satisfied by the same values of the unknown quantities.

Examples:

$y = 2x$ has many solutions:
$\{\ldots(^-1, \,^-2), (0, 0), (1, 2), (2, 4), (3, 6)\ldots\}$

$x + y = 3$ has many solutions:
$\{\ldots(^-1, 4), (0, 3), (1, 2), (2, 1), (3, 0)\ldots\}$

but if $\left.\begin{array}{l} y = 2x \\ x + y = 3 \end{array}\right\}$ are taken as simultaneous equations there is only one solution, (1, 2) that is $x = 1$ and $y = 2$.

If simultaneous equations are shown *graphically*, the solution is given by the *intersection(s)* of the lines.

Examples:

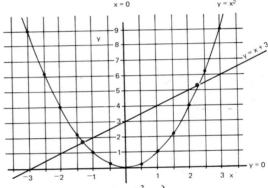

$\left.\begin{array}{l} y = 2x \\ x + y = 3 \end{array}\right\}$ have solution

$x = 1$ and $y = 2$

$\left.\begin{array}{l} y = x^2 \\ y = x + 3 \end{array}\right\}$ have solutions

$x = \,^-1.3$ and $y = 1.7$

AND

$x = 2.3$ and $y = 5.3$

Sine

The sine of an *angle* θ is written as $\sin \theta$

Sine of angles less than 90°

$$\sin \theta = \frac{BC}{AG} \qquad \sin \theta = \frac{\text{opposite side}}{\text{hypotenuse}}$$

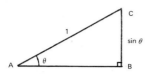

When the length of AC is 1 then
$$\sin \theta = BC$$

When this *triangle* is *enlarged*, with *scale factor* r,
$$QR = r \sin \theta$$

Examples:

$$\sin x = \tfrac{3}{5}$$
$$\sin x = 0.6$$
$$\sin 36.9° = 0.600$$
$$x = 36.9°$$

$QR = 3 \sin 30°$ $(\sin 30° = 0.5$ from
      $= 3 \times 0.5$ tables)
      $= 1.5$

Sine of any angle

If a line OP of unit length turns through an angle θ from the
x-*axis*; then the sine of θ is the y-*coordinate* of P shown in red.

Sine rule

When the lengths of two sides of a *triangle* and an angle (not
the one formed by the two sides) are known, then a second angle
can be found by the rule

$$\frac{a}{\sin A} = \frac{b}{\sin B}$$

When two angles and the length of one side of a triangle are
known, then another side can be found using the same rule.

Slant height

Slant height of a cone

When a *cone* has a *circle* for a base and the *vertex* is above the centre of the base, then the cone is a right circular cone. For such a cone, the slant height is the length of a straight line from the vertex to the circle forming the base.

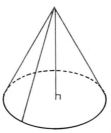

For this cone the slant height is represented by the red lines.

Slant height of a pyramid

When a *pyramid* has a *regular polygon* for a base and the *apex* is above the centre of the base, then the pyramid is a regular pyramid. For such a pyramid, the slant height is the length of a line from the apex *perpendicular* to an edge of the base.

For this pyramid the slant height is represented by the red line.

Solution of an equation

The solution of an *equation* is the *set* of numbers which, when put instead of the letters, make the statement true.

Examples:
$4 + x = 11$ has solution $x = 7$ because $4 + 7 = 11$
$2 \times x = 10$ has solution $x = 5$ because $2 \times 5 = 10$
$y - 3 = 5$ has solution $y = 8$ because $8 - 3 = 5$
$x^2 = 9$ has two solutions $x = 3$ and $x = {}^-3$
$y = x + 3$ has many solutions; one solution is $x = 2$, $y = 5$ which can be written using *ordered pairs* as $(2, 5)$
The *solution set* for $y = x + 3$ with x and y being *integers*, is
$\{\ldots({}^-1, 2), (0, 3), (1, 4), (2, 5),\ldots\}$

Solution set

When the *solution of an equation* or *inequality* is more than one number or pair, then the solution is usually called a solution *set*.

Examples:

$x^2 = 4$ has the solution set $\{x = {}^+2, \text{ or } x = {}^-2\}$
or $\{x: \quad x = {}^+2 \text{ or } {}^-2\}$

For x a *counting number*, $2x > 6$ has the solution set
$\{x > 3\}$ or $\{x: x > 3\}$
or $\{4, 5, 6, 7, 8, 9, 10, 11, \ldots\}$

Because a solution set often has many members it is helpful to show it *graphically*.

Examples:

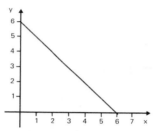

For x and y *real*, $x + y = 6$ has the solution set shown by the red line, that is $\{(x, y): \quad x + y = 6\}$

For p and q *integers*, $p + q \leqslant 5$, $p > 0$ and $q > 0$, has the solution set shown by the red dots, that is
$\{(1, 1), (1, 2), (1, 3), (1, 4), (2, 1), (2, 2), (2, 3), (3, 1), (3, 2), (4, 1)\}$

The solution sets are shown in red:

for x real, and $x > 3$ it is

for x an integer and $0 < x \leqslant 4$ it is

for x an integer and $^-1 \leqslant x \leqslant 4$ it is

for x real and $^-2 < x \leqslant 4$ it is

Speed

The speed of a body is the distance travelled by the body per unit of time.

Examples:

A car travels along a motorway for 2 hours at the same speed and goes 142 *kilometres*. The speed at which the car is travelling is

$$\frac{142 \text{ kilometres}}{2 \text{ hours}} = 71 \text{ kilometres per hour}$$

$$= 71 \text{ km/h}$$

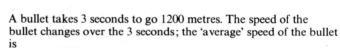

A bullet takes 3 seconds to go 1200 metres. The speed of the bullet changes over the 3 seconds; the 'average' speed of the bullet is

$$\frac{1200 \text{ metres}}{3 \text{ seconds}} = 400 \text{ m/s}$$

For a body whose speed is changing, its speed at an instant is represented on a distance-time *graph* by the *gradient* of the curve at that instant.

Example: A marble rolls down a slope and the distance travelled is shown by this graph.

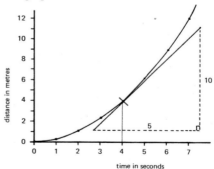

The speed of the marble after 4 seconds is given by the gradient of the red line:

$$\frac{10 \text{ metres}}{5 \text{ seconds}} = 2 \text{ m/s}$$

See **Acceleration, Velocity**

Sphere

A sphere is the mathematical name for a perfectly round ball.

Examples:

A soap bubble blown into the air is very nearly a sphere.

The Earth and the other planets are roughly spheres.

A sphere is the *set* of points in space which are all the same distance, called the *radius*, from a fixed point called the centre.

If the radius is r then the surface *area* of the sphere is given by

$A = 4\pi r^2$

and the *volume* of the solid formed by the sphere is given by

$V = \frac{4}{3}\pi r^3$

Square

A square is a *rectangle* with four equal sides.
A square is a *regular quadrilateral*.

Examples:

wall tiles

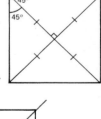

A square has:
- a) four *lines of symmetry*;
- b) *rotational symmetry* of *order* 4;
- c) opposite sides *parallel*;
- d) all four *angles* of the figure equal to 90°;
- e) *diagonals* equal and *bisecting* each other at *right-angles*.

Square centimetre

A square centimetre is a *unit* for measuring *area* and is equal
to the area of a *square* whose sides are one *centimetre* in length.
Square centimetre is shortened to cm^2

Examples:

This area [1 cm square] is 1 cm^2

The area of A is
6 cm × 9 cm = 54 cm^2

The area of the *triangle* is $\frac{1}{2}$ of 3 × 5 cm^2
= $\frac{1}{2}$ × 15 cm^2
= 7.5 cm^2

Square metre

A square metre is the standard *unit* for measuring *area*. One
square metre is the same area as a *square* whose sides are one
metre in length. Square metre is shortened to m^2

Examples:

This area is 1 m^2

The area of
this room is
4 × 6 m^2
= 24 m^2

The area of this wall is 3.5 × 3 m^2
= 10.5 m^2

NOTE:

1 m^2 = 100 × 100 cm^2
1 m^2 = 10000 cm^2

Square number

A square number is a number that can be shown as a pattern of dots in the shape of a *square*.

Examples:

$4 = 2 \times 2$ $16 = 4 \times 4$ $25 = 5 \times 5$

{square numbers} = {1, 4, 9, 16, 25, 36, 49, 64, 81, 100,...}

NOTE: The number 1 is a square number but not a *rectangle number*.

Square of a number

The square of a number is that number multiplied by itself. We often say it is the number 'squared'.

Example: 6 squared is 36

A number squared means the same as the number to the *power* of 2.

Square root

The square root of a number N can be thought of, as the length of a side of a *square* whose *area* is N. It is the number which when *squared* is equal to N.

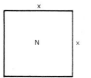

side of square   area of square

     x   N

x is the square root of N which is written

$x = \sqrt{N}$

Examples:

side   area

 3   9 $3 = \sqrt{9}$

$\sqrt{36} = 6$ $\sqrt{49} = 7$ $\sqrt{1} = 1$ $\sqrt{0.25} = 0.5$

NOTE: The *equation* $x^2 = 4$ has two *solutions* $x = {}^{+}\sqrt{4}$ and $x = {}^{-}\sqrt{4}$

that is

$x = {}^{+}2$ and $x = {}^{-}2$.

Standard index form

A number is in standard (*index*) *form*, when it is written as a
number between 1 and 10 multiplied by a *power* of 10.

Examples:

$$400000 = 4 \times 10^5$$
$$9650000 = 9.65 \times 10^6$$
$$1013 = 1.013 \times 10^3$$
$$0.00308 = 3.08 \times 10^{-3}$$
$$7.896 = 7.896 \times 10^0$$
$$= 7.896 \times 1$$
$$= 7.896$$

Stretches

One-way stretch

A stretch is a *transformation* in which shapes are pulled or
stretched in one direction.

Examples (left):

The red shapes show the *images* of the black shapes after a stretch
across the page.

There is an *invariant* line, and all other points move on lines
perpendicular to this line.

Example:

The red line is invariant and
A′B′C′ is the image after a stretch
in the direction of the x-*axis*.

Lines PAA′ and QBB′ are perpendicular
to the invariant line.

There is a linear *scale factor* k which gives the amount of stretch.
For any point A, with line PA perpendicular to the invariant
line s, its image A′ is given by
$$PA' = k \times PA$$

Example: The invariant line is x = 0. The image after a stretch
with scale factor 3 is shown in red.

Stretch matrix

The transformation $\begin{pmatrix} x \\ y \end{pmatrix} \rightarrow \begin{pmatrix} 1 & 0 \\ 0 & k \end{pmatrix} \begin{pmatrix} x \\ y \end{pmatrix}$

represents a stretch with $y = 0$ invariant and scale factor k.

Two-way stretch

A two-way stretch is the single transformation representing stretches with two different invariant lines.

Example:
The image A′B′C′D′ shows the two-way stretch on ABCD:

$x = 0$ invariant and scale factor 2,
$y = 0$ invariant and scale factor 3.

Structure

Many *sets* of *elements* have *operations* on them which show similar properties.

For an operation ∗ on a set, some of the properties we ask for are:

a) is the operation ∗ on the set *closed*?
b) is there an *identity* element in the set?
c) if there is an identity element, does each element of the set have an *inverse* in the set?
d) does the operation ∗ on the set show that it is
   i) *associative*?
   ii) *commutative*?
   and, when there is a second operation ∘ on the same set, that
   iii) ∗ is *distributive* over ∘?

A set with an operation which has the four properties of closure, identity, inverse, and associativity is called a group.

Examples:

The following sets with operations are each a group:

   Numbers under addition;
   Numbers (omitting *zero*) under multiplication;
   Vectors under addition;
   Isometries of the *plane* under 'follows';
   The set of all 2 by 2 *matrices* (with *determinant* not zero) under
                              matrix multiplication.

In a group, every *equation* $a * x = b$ or $x * a = b$ has a unique *solution*.

Subset

If every *element* of *set* B is also an element of the set A then B is a subset of A.

Example: If A is {a, b, c, d} then all the possible subsets B of set A are:

{a} {b} {c} {d} {a,b} {a,c} {a,d}
{b,c} {b,d} {c,d} {b,c,d} {a,c,d}
{a,b,d} {a,b,c} {a,b,c,d} and {}

When B is a subset of A we write B ⊂ A

NOTE: In the example above, all the subsets except {} and {a, b, c, d} are PROPER SUBSETS of A.

Subtend an angle

The angle subtended by two points A and B at a point P is the *angle* between the lines AP and BP.

Examples:

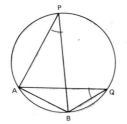

The angle subtended by a *chord* AB of a *circle* at a point P on its *circumference* is equal to the angle it subtends at Q.

The angle subtended by the end points C, D of a *diameter* of a circle at a point T on its circumference is a *right-angle*.

Subtract

Subtract is the mathematical word for 'take away'.

Sum

Sum is the mathematical word for 'add up'.

Supplementary angles

If two *angles*, such as 115° and 65° add up to 180° they are called supplementary angles.

115° + 65° = 180°.

115° and 65° are supplementary angles.

The opposite angles of a cyclic *quadrilateral* are always supplementary.
$x + y = 180°$

Surd

A surd is an *irrational number*.
Examples: $\sqrt{2}, \quad \sqrt{3}, \quad \sqrt{7} + 1, \quad 9 - \sqrt{3}, \quad \sqrt{8}, \quad \sqrt[3]{16}$

Symbols

Mathematical symbols are the signs that we use in mathematics.
Examples:

$$+ \quad - \quad \times \quad \div \quad \cap \quad \cup \quad \in \quad \notin$$
$$\{\} \quad = \quad < \quad > \quad Q \quad \mathbb{Z}$$

Symmetry

Symmetry is the kind of pattern that a shape has.

Symmetry of plane shapes
There are two kinds of symmetry that a *plane shape* can have:
a) *line symmetry*;
   This shape has one line of symmetry shown in red;

b) *rotational symmetry*;
   This shape has rotational symmetry of *order* three.

Symmetry of solid shapes
There are three kinds of symmetry that a solid can have:
a) *plane symmetry*;
   This fish has one plane of symmetry shown in red;

b) *rotational symmetry*;
   This propeller has rotational symmetry of order four.

c) *point symmetry*;
   This solid has point symmetry.

   The full symmetry of a solid is called its *symmetry number*.

Symmetry number

The symmetry number of a solid is the number of ways it can be put into a mould of the shape.

Example:

The red shading shows the four ways in which this solid can be put into a mould. The symmetry number for the *cuboid* is 4.

Tangent of an angle

The tangent of an *angle* θ is written as tan θ.

Tangent of angles less than 90°

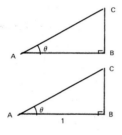

$$\tan \theta = \frac{BC}{AB} \qquad \tan \theta = \frac{\text{opposite side}}{\text{adjacent side}}$$

When the length of AB is 1 then
$\tan \theta = BC$

When this *triangle* is *enlarged*,
with *scale factor* r, QR = r tan θ

Examples:
$\tan x = \frac{3}{4}$
$\tan x = 0.75$
$\tan 36.9° = 0.751$ (from tables)
$x = 36.9°$

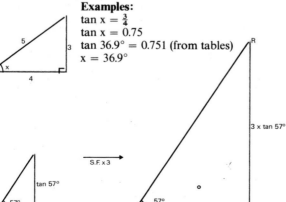

$$QR = 3 \times \tan 57°$$
$$= 3 \times 1.54$$
$$= 4.62$$

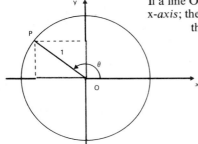

Tangent of any angle

If a line OP of unit length turns through an angle θ from the x-*axis*; then

the tangent of θ is the *ratio* $\dfrac{\text{y-coordinate}}{\text{x-coordinate}}$

If P is (x, y) then

$$\tan \theta = \frac{y}{x}$$

and $\tan \theta = \dfrac{\sin \theta}{\cos \theta}$

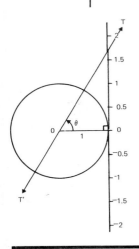

If TOT′ extends without limit in the direction T and in the direction T′, with O the centre of a *circle radius* 1; then the tangent of an angle θ, formed as the line TOT′ turns as shown, is the intercept made by either end of the line TOT′ with the number line.

The length of the red line is tan θ.

See **Gradient**

Tangent to a curve

The tangent to a curve is the straight line 'just' touching the curve.

Examples:

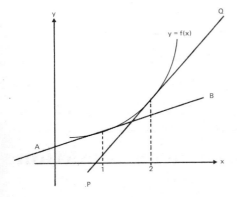

The line AB is the tangent to the curve y = f(x) when x = 1

The line PQ is the tangent to the curve y = f(x) when x = 2

Terminating decimal

A *fraction* can be written as a terminating decimal if it can be worked out exactly, without *recurring*.

Examples:

$\frac{3}{4} = 0.75$ $\frac{7}{16} = 0.4375$ $\frac{9}{640} = 0.0140625$

But $\frac{2}{3} = 0.6666\ldots$ does not terminate.

NOTE: A fraction which terminates as a decimal has a *denominator* with only 2 and 5 as *prime factors*.

Tessellation

A tessellation is a way of covering the *plane* with *polygons* to form a regular pattern.

Examples:

Tetrahedron

A tetrahedron is a solid with four *triangular faces*. It is the same as a triangular-based *pyramid*.

Examples:

This is a *regular* tetrahedron; all four faces are *equilateral triangles*.

Tonne

A tonne is a *unit* of mass. One tonne is equal to 1000 *kilograms*. We shorten tonne to t

Example (left): This Rover car has a mass of about one tonne.

Topological transformation

see **Topology**

Topologically equivalent

A shape and its *image* after any *topological transformation* are said to be topologically equivalent.

Examples: The red images show some possible topological transformations of the black circle. This gives the *set* of topologically equivalent shapes shown below.

Topology

Topology is the study of what happens to a shape if it is drawn on a thin elastic sheet, so that it can be pulled and stretched. It is sometimes called 'rubber sheet geometry'.

Example:

This kind of change is a topological *transformation*. The shape must NOT be torn, and must NOT be joined together, only given twists and stretches (in any direction).

Here are some of the facts that are *invariant* under a topological transformation:
a) the number of *nodes*;
b) the *order* of each node;
c) the number of *arcs*;
d) the order of points along each arc;
e) the number of *regions*.

In the hierarchy of *transformations*, topological transformations come after the *isometries* and the *similarities*. They allow for more distortions but still enough properties are *invariant* for the transformation to be useful.

Example: This British Rail map showing Inter-City Services between London and Scotland is a topological transformation of the actual railway lines.

identity

↓

isometries

↓

similarities

↓

affine transformations

↓

topological transformations

Transformation

When we are *mapping* points and lines, rather than numbers, we use the word transformation.

A transformation describes the *relation* between any point and its *image* point.

The hierarchy of transformations usually considered, is shown at the side. Under these headings we find such transformations as *rotations, reflections, translations,* and *enlargements.*

Translation

A translation is a *transformation* in which a shape slides without turning. Every point moves the same distance and the same direction.

Examples:

In each case the red shape is the *image* after a translation

A translation can be described by a *vector.*

Examples:

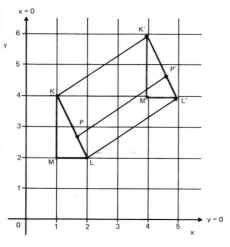

The red triangle shows the image of triangle KLM after a translation

described by the vector $\begin{pmatrix} 3 \\ 2 \end{pmatrix}$

K (1, 4) *maps onto* K'(4, 6)
L (2, 2) is mapped onto L' (5, 4)

by the translation $\begin{pmatrix} 3 \\ 2 \end{pmatrix}$

If P is (x, y) its image P' is found by

$$\begin{pmatrix} x \\ y \end{pmatrix} \rightarrow \begin{pmatrix} x + 3 \\ y + 2 \end{pmatrix}$$

The image A'B'C'D' is shown in red for a translation of ABCD.
Each point has moved the same distance and direction, described by vector **a**.
The vector **a** can be represented by this line

Transpose

The transpose of a *matrix* **A** is the matrix **A'** made by changing over the *rows* and *columns*.

Example:

$$\text{If } \mathbf{A} = \begin{pmatrix} 2 & 0 \\ 1 & 2 \\ 1 & 0 \end{pmatrix} \quad \text{then } \mathbf{A'} = \begin{pmatrix} 2 & 1 & 1 \\ 0 & 2 & 0 \end{pmatrix}$$

If the matrix **A** represents a *relation*, then the matrix **A'** represents the inverse relation.

Example: For the family Harry, John, Ian and Katie, the relation '——is the parent of——' can be shown on an *arrow diagram*, or by means of a matrix.

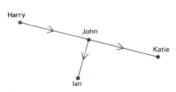

$$\mathbf{P} = \begin{array}{c} \\ \text{H} \\ \text{I} \\ \text{J} \\ \text{K} \end{array} \begin{array}{cccc} \text{H} & \text{I} & \text{J} & \text{K} \\ \begin{pmatrix} 0 & 0 & 1 & 0 \\ 0 & 0 & 0 & 0 \\ 0 & 1 & 0 & 1 \\ 0 & 0 & 0 & 0 \end{pmatrix} \end{array}$$

The transpose of **P**, **P'**, shows the relation '——is the child of——'

$$\mathbf{P'} = \begin{pmatrix} 0 & 0 & 0 & 0 \\ 0 & 0 & 1 & 0 \\ 1 & 0 & 0 & 0 \\ 0 & 0 & 1 & 0 \end{pmatrix}$$

Trapezium

A trapezium is a *quadrilateral* with ONE pair of sides *parallel*.

Examples:

The *area* of a trapezium with parallel sides of length a and b is given by
Area of Trapezium = $\frac{1}{2}$ (a + b) × Height

Traversable

A *network* is traversable if it can be drawn without taking the pen off the paper, or going over the same line twice.

Example (left):

The black network is traversable. One possible way of drawing it is shown by the red line.

A network is traversable if either:
a) there are only two odd nodes: (start at one odd node, finish at the other odd node); or
b) there are all even nodes: (start at any point on any *arc*, finish at the starting point). See **Unicursal**

See **Equilateral Triangle,
Isosceles Triangle,
Right-angled Triangle,**
and **Scalene Triangle**

Triangle

A triangle is a *plane shape* made with three straight sides.

Examples:

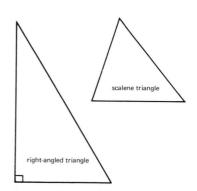

equilateral triangle

isosceles triangle

right-angled triangle

scalene triangle

Triangle number

A triangle number is the number that can be shown as a pattern of dots in the shape of a *triangle*.

Examples:

3   6   10   15

{triangle numbers} = {1, 3, 6, 10, 15, 21, 28, 36, 45,...}

NOTE:
$10 = 1 + 2 + 3 + 4$
$21 = 1 + 2 + 3 + 4 + 5 + 6$
$36 = 1 + 2 + 3 + 4 + 5 + 6 + 7 + 8$

Unicursal

A unicursal curve is a curve drawn without going over the same *arc* twice, and with the finish joined to the start.

Examples:

NOTE: All unicursal curves are *traversable networks* with even *nodes*.

Only two colours are needed to colour the *regions* formed by a unicursal curve. Touching regions must not have the same colour.

Union

The union of two *sets* A and B is the set of *elements* that are in A, or in B, or are in both A and B.

Example:

> If A = {1, 4, 7, 11, 14}
> and B = {2, 4, 10, 14}
> then A ∪ B = {1, 2, 4, 7, 10, 11, 14}

The union of sets is shown by the *symbol* ∪

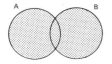

On a *Venn diagram* the union of set A and set B is shown by the set of points shaded red.
A ∪ B is shaded red.

Units of measurement

The standard unit for measuring length is a *metre*. Two smaller units of length are *millimetre* and *centimetre*. A larger unit of length than a metre is a *kilometre*.

The units for *area* are usually *square centimetre* or *square metre*. Another unit sometimes used for large areas is hectare. One hectare is 10000 m^2.

The units for *volume* are usually *cubic centimetre* or *cubic metre*. Another unit sometimes used for liquids or gases is *litre*.

The standard unit for measuring mass is a *kilogram*. A smaller unit of mass is *gram*. A larger unit that is sometimes used is *tonne*.

Universal set

The universal set is the set of ALL *elements* being considered. We use the *symbol $\mathscr{E}$* to represent the universal set.

Example:
If $\mathscr{E} = \{$*counting numbers* less than 10$\}$
and A = $\{$*prime numbers*$\}$
then A$'$ = $\{1, 4, 6, 8, 9\}$

On a *Venn diagram* the universal set is shown by a *rectangle*.

Example:
$\mathscr{E} = \{$counting numbers less than 10$\}$
A = $\{$prime numbers$\}$

See **Complement of a Set**

Variable

When letters such as x and y are used in *formulas* and mathematical *expressions* to stand for different numbers they are called variables, in contrast to letters which have a fixed value and are called *constants*.

Examples:
In the formula for the area for a circle, $A = \pi r^2$, r and A are variables, but π is a constant.

In the equation for a straight line, such as $y = 3x + 2$, x and y are variables, but 2 and 3 are constants.

See **Coefficient**

Vector

A vector is a number store. It is usually shown as a *column* of numbers like this

$$\begin{pmatrix} 2 \\ -3 \\ 6 \end{pmatrix} \quad \begin{pmatrix} 1 \\ 7 \end{pmatrix} \quad \begin{pmatrix} 0 \\ 4 \\ 18 \\ 0 \\ 1 \end{pmatrix}$$

Each number in the number store means something different. The column of numbers is treated as just ONE number called a vector. We often describe a vector by using a letter. The letter must be either underlined with a 'squiggle' like this $\underset{\sim}{a}$ or printed in 'bold type' like this **a**.

Examples:

$$\underset{\sim}{P} = \begin{pmatrix} 3 \\ 2 \\ -5 \end{pmatrix} \quad \mathbf{b} = \begin{pmatrix} 1 \\ 0 \end{pmatrix}$$

$2 + a = 5$.
Here a is an ordinary number, known sometimes as a scalar, $a = 3$.

$$\begin{pmatrix} 1 \\ 4 \end{pmatrix} + \begin{pmatrix} 2 \\ 3 \end{pmatrix} = \mathbf{a}. \text{ Here } \mathbf{a} \text{ is a vector, } \mathbf{a} = \begin{pmatrix} 3 \\ 7 \end{pmatrix}$$

Vectors as ordered sets
Vectors act like shopping lists, in which the order of the items matter.

Example:
If the vector represents a shopping list for butter, milk, eggs, and bread, each list must show the items in this same order.

2 kg of butter, no milk, 12 eggs, and 1 loaf is $\begin{pmatrix} 2 \\ 0 \\ 12 \\ 1 \end{pmatrix}$

With a friend's list of $\begin{pmatrix} 3 \\ 1 \\ 6 \\ 0 \end{pmatrix}$ the shopping lists together are

$$\begin{pmatrix} 2 \\ 0 \\ 12 \\ 1 \end{pmatrix} + \begin{pmatrix} 3 \\ 1 \\ 6 \\ 0 \end{pmatrix} = \begin{pmatrix} 5 \\ 1 \\ 18 \\ 1 \end{pmatrix}$$

Vectors as displacements
Vectors can be used to describe *journeys* or *displacements*.

Example:
The journey shown in red is 3 across and 2 up, or as a vector, **d**

$$\mathbf{d} = \begin{pmatrix} 3 \\ 2 \end{pmatrix}.$$

Vector quantities
Some physical quantities are described by both a size and a direction. These quantities are vector quantities.
Quantities like time, which have no direction are scalar quantities.

Examples:
Displacement is a vector but distance and length are scalar quantities.
Velocity is a vector but *speed* is a scalar.

Vectors to describe translations
In a *translation* every point moves the same displacement, so ONE vector will describe the translation.

Example (left):
The black shape is given a translation. The image is shown in red.

For any point P, the displacement P to P′ is described by
the vector $\mathbf{a} = \begin{pmatrix} 6 \\ 2 \end{pmatrix}$. So this translation is the translation $\begin{pmatrix} 6 \\ 2 \end{pmatrix}$.

Scalar multiplying of a vector

When a vector is multiplied by a scalar (an ordinary number) each item in the vector is multiplied by the scalar.

$$k \times \begin{pmatrix} a_1 \\ a_2 \\ a_3 \end{pmatrix} = \begin{pmatrix} ka_1 \\ ka_2 \\ ka_3 \end{pmatrix}$$

Examples:

If $\mathbf{a} = \begin{pmatrix} 2 \\ 1 \\ 7 \end{pmatrix}$, then $3\mathbf{a} = 3\begin{pmatrix} 2 \\ 1 \\ 7 \end{pmatrix} = \begin{pmatrix} 6 \\ 3 \\ 21 \end{pmatrix}$

If $\mathbf{p} = k\mathbf{q}$, where k is a scalar,
then $\mathbf{p}$, shown in red, is k times the length of $\mathbf{q}$ and *parallel* to $\mathbf{q}$.

Vector addition

The addition of vectors can be performed by adding corresponding items.

$$\begin{pmatrix} a_1 \\ a_2 \\ a_3 \end{pmatrix} + \begin{pmatrix} b_1 \\ b_2 \\ b_3 \end{pmatrix} = \begin{pmatrix} a_1 + b_1 \\ a_2 + b_2 \\ a_3 + b_3 \end{pmatrix}$$

Example:

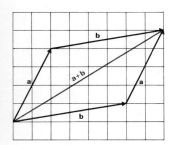

If $\mathbf{a} = \begin{pmatrix} 2 \\ 4 \end{pmatrix}$ and $\mathbf{b} = \begin{pmatrix} 6 \\ 1 \end{pmatrix}$

then $\mathbf{a} + \mathbf{b} = \begin{pmatrix} 2 \\ 4 \end{pmatrix} + \begin{pmatrix} 6 \\ 1 \end{pmatrix}$

$$= \begin{pmatrix} 8 \\ 5 \end{pmatrix}$$

NOTE: The addition of vectors is *commutative*, $\mathbf{a} + \mathbf{b} = \mathbf{b} + \mathbf{a}$

Velocity

Velocity is a measure of the *speed* with which a body moves in a particular direction. Velocity is a *vector* quantity.

Example: A car whose speed is 40 metre/second has a velocity of 40 metre/second due north if it is travelling in a northerly direction. If the car then proceeds in an easterly direction with the same speed, 40 metre/second, it has a different velocity.

Venn diagram

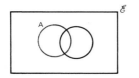

A Venn diagram is used to show *sets*. Each set is represented by the *region* inside a *simple closed curve*, usually a *circle*, and the *universal set* is shown by a *rectangle*.

Example:

Any *element* of set A must be INSIDE the red circle.
Any element not in set A must be OUTSIDE the red circle.

Example:

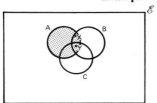

The set A is all the points in the region shaded red.
X and Y are in set A.
X is also in set B.
Y is also in both set B and set C.

Vertex (plural Vertices)

A vertex is a corner of a shape (or solid). In a *polygon* it is the point where the sides meet.

Examples:

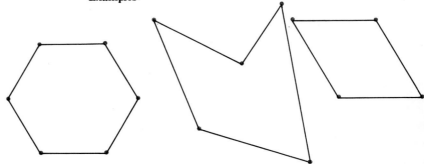

The vertices of these shapes are shown by red dots.

In a *polyhedron*, it is the point where the edges meet.

Examples:
All the vertices of this *cube*
are shown by red dots.

A *cone* only has one vertex, and is shown on the cone above by a red dot.

Vertical

A line is vertical if it is *parallel* to a string with a weight hanging on the end. Builders use a weight on the end of a string to enable them to build walls vertically.

Example (left): The red line shows the vertical line through the string.

NOTE: Any object which is dropped follows a line which is vertical.

Volume

The volume of a solid is the amount of space it occupies.

Example:
The volume of a *cuboid* measuring 3 cm by 4 cm by 5 cm:

The bottom layer has $4 \times 5 = 20$ cubes
There are 3 layers,
total number of cubes,
$3 \times 20 = 60$ cubes
Volume of cuboid $= 3 \times 4 \times 5$
$= 60 \text{ cm}^3$

The *units* of measurement are usually *cubic centimetre*, or *cubic metre*.
Most volumes can be found by two *formulas*:

Volumes of prisms
The volume of *prisms*, including *cuboid* and *cylinder* is given by
$V = A \times h$
where A is the *area* of the end and h is the height or length of the prism.

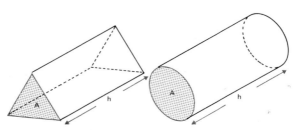

Volumes of pyramids
The volume of *pyramids*, and also the *cone* is given by
$V = \frac{1}{3} \times A \times h$
where A is the area of the base and h is the *perpendicular* height.

Whole numbers

The *set* of whole numbers is the set whose *members* are *zero* and the *counting numbers*.

{whole numbers} = {0, 1, 2, 3, 4, 5, 6, 7, 8, . . .}

NOTE: The *natural numbers* or counting numbers, are not usually considered to include zero.

Zero

Zero is shown by the *symbol* 0 (*nought*). Zero has several meanings.

a) Zero is used to show an empty place value in a number with more than one *digit*.

Examples:

2039 means
> 2 thousands
> NO hundreds
> 3 tens
> 9 units

405 means
> 4 hundreds
> NO tens
> 5 units.

b) Zero is the *identity* for the addition of numbers.

Examples:

$$3 + 0 = 3$$
$$7 + 0 = 7$$
$$^-4 + 0 = {}^-4$$
$$0 + 2 = 2$$
$$0 + 1 = 1$$
$$^-5 + 0 = {}^-5$$

c) Zero is the point on the number line between the *positive* numbers and the *negative* numbers.

d) Zero is the number of *elements* in the *empty set*.

n(ø) = 0